American National Standard Practice for

ROADWAY LIGHTING

**Illuminating Engineering Society
of North America**

Approved by the
American National Standards Institute
July 21, 1983

ISBN 0-87995-013-7
Library of Congress Cataloging pending.

Published by the
Illuminating Engineering Society of North America
345 East 47th Street
New York, NY 10017

Printed in the United States of America

Contents

American National Standard Practice for Roadway Lighting

Prepared by the IES Roadway Lighting Committee
Richard N. Schwab, Chairman, 1982–83
S. Howard Young, Chairman, 1981–82

J. E. Alvarado	T. E. Lewis
* J. B. Arens	D. P. Loyd
V. R. Bishop	A. Lurkis
P. C. Box	* M. V. Massaro
J. R. Brass	J. R. McCormick
* J. A. Buck	V. A. McCullough
J. C. Busser	S. W. McKnight
E. Cacique	H. D. Mosley
P. Careaga	H. A. Odle
G. E. Chamberlain	C. A. Oerkvitz
J. L. Clapper	D. P. Palmer
* F. Clark	E. C. Rowsell
P. G. Contos	B. L. Shelby
J. T. Cottingham	M. E. Siska
C. W. Craig	R. L. Sitzema
* D. L. Crawford	* G. E. Smallwood
L. H. Cronan	* G. M. Smith
C. L. Crouch	* E. B. Spurr
R. K. Drake	R. E. Stark
** W. K. Edman	A. E. Tanner
K. E. Fairbanks	* J. E. Tewart
R. E. Faucett	C. L. Thomas
* V. P. Gallagher	M. C. Unglert
R. W. Godemann	H. A. Vandusen
E. O. Heinlein	S. C. Varnum
* D. A. Hiatt	* R. L. Vincent
D. E. Husby	* M. J. Vitartas
M. S. Janoff	* J. E. Wagner
J. E. Jewell	V. H. Waight
M. E. Keck	* I. Weinstein
A. Ketvirtis	G. W. Weist
I. Kopec	A. R. Wilson
* J. Lapporte	R. R. Wylie
* R. C. LeVere	R. E. Young
I. Lewin	

* Advisory
** Honorary

During the 57-year career of the IES's Committee on Roadway Lighting, the night use of public ways has grown greatly. Traffic has changed in speed and density. Studies by the committee have established a substantial relationship between good fixed lighting and traffic safety. In addition, understanding of the principles of good lighting has advanced. The following earlier publications of the committee reflect progress of the roadway lighting technique through the years.

Principles of Streetlighting	1928
Code of Streetlighting	1930
Code of Streetlighting	1935
Code of Streetlighting	1937
Recommended Practice of Streetlighting	1940
Recommended Practice of Street and Highway Lighting	1945
American Standard Practice for Street and Highway Lighting	1947
American Standard Practice for Street and Highway Lighting	1953
American Standard Practice for Roadway Lighting	1963
American National Standard Practice for Roadway Lighting	1972
American National Standard Practice for Roadway Lighting	1977

The present Standard Practice has evolved out of these earlier documents, and considers the latest research, experience, and equipment technology.

An American National Standard represents the national consensus of all groups having an essential interest in the provisions of the Standard Practice. The IES, as sponsor, must have the viewpoints of all groups interested in roadway lighting represented on a Roadway Lighting Committee.

Foreword

(This Foreword is not a part of the "American National Standard Practice for Roadway Lighting, ANSI/IES RP-8, 1983," but is included for information purposes only.)

This "American National Standard Practice for Roadway Lighting" has been approved under the rules of procedure of the American National Standards Institute and under the sponsorship of the Illuminating Engineering Society of North America (IES). This document has been revised from the 1977 Standard Practice to include, in addition to an illuminance method for design, a luminance method that incorporates veiling luminance. Although the luminance method is preferred for most situations, illuminance is regarded as an acceptable alternative. Design and calculations are now specified in metric units. Changes in the Appendices (which are not part of the Standard Practice but are provided as supplemental information) include a new Appendix on visibility and one containing metric conversion tables.

Approved December 8, 1982 by the Board of Directors of the Illuminating Engineering Society of North America as a Transaction of the Society.

1. Introduction

1.1 Purpose of Standard Practice. The primary purpose of this Standard Practice is to serve as the basis for design of fixed lighting for roadways, bikeways, and pedestrian ways. The Standard Practice deals entirely with lighting and does not give advice on construction practice. It is neither intended as, nor does it establish a legal standard for roadway lighting systems. Its purpose is to provide recommended practices for designing new roadway lighting systems, and it is not intended to be applied to existing lighting systems until such systems are redesigned. It has been prepared to advance the art, science, and practice of illumination as it pertains to roadway lighting in North America.

The decision to provide roadway lighting at a particular location should be made on the basis of a detailed study. Thus, the publication is not a substitute for reasoned judgment. Variations may be considered from this Standard Practice based upon sound engineering judgment.

1.2 Purpose of roadway lighting. (1) The principal purpose of roadway lighting is to produce quick, accurate, and comfortable seeing at night. These qualities of seeing may safeguard, facilitate, and encourage vehicular and pedestrian traffic. Every designer should provide for those inherent qualities required by the user. A very important consideration is that of making streets and highways useful during hours of darkness as well as during the daytime. Where good seeing is provided through illumination, efficient night use can be made of the large investments in roadways and motor vehicles. Thus, the proper use of roadway lighting as an operative tool provides economic and social benefits to the public including:

(a) Reduction in night accidents, attendant human misery, and economic loss

(b) Aid to police protection

(c) Facilitation of traffic flow

(d) Promotion of business and industries during the night hours

(e) Inspiration for community spirit and growth

(2) This Standard Practice is for fixed lighting of the different kinds of public roads, pedestrian walkways and bikeways of a quality considered appropriate to modern requirements for night use. Where lighting has been installed, the result has often been a marked reduction in night accidents. Pedestrian and vehicular traffic has been expedited. Practicability and economy have been demonstrated.

1.3 Sources of nightime illumination. The nighttime illumination available for providing visibility for the driver comes from three sources:

(a) The fixed lighting system covered by this Standard Practice

(b) Extraneous off-roadway light sources and

(c) The vehicle headlighting system

For discussion of vehicular lighting refer to publications of the Society of Automotive Engineers (SAE).

1.4 Night/day accident relationship. (1) Darkness brings increased hazards to users of streets and highways because it reduces the distance they can see. The fatal accident rate at night is about three times greater than the daytime rate, based on proportional vehicle kilometers of travel. There are additional factors that interact at night with reduced visibility conditions and account in part for the higher accident rate. These factors are:

(a) Glare from extraneous background lighting

(b) Lack of environmental clues (or recognition clues)

(c) Defective, inadequate, improperly maintained, or misused vehicle lighting

(d) Increased driver fatigue

(e) Increased use of alcohol and other drugs

(f) Declining visual capability (perception, adaptation, accommodation, and glare tolerance), particularly for the older driver, at the lower lighting levels available at night.

All of these factors interact with each other.

Therefore, it is difficult, if not impossible, to attribute the increase in accident rate at night to any single cause. However, lack of adequate visual information will make each of the above factors worse and will greatly degrade the driver's already limited abilities to respond correctly.

(2) Experience has demonstrated that under many circumstances prevailing in North America, it is possible to light urban and suburban streets, and the critical sections of highways, so as to reduce the excessive toll of lives attributable to inadequate visibility. Furthermore, the IES Roadway Lighting Committee is of the opinion that such improvements in the lighting of streets and highways generally are economically practicable. These preventive measures can cost a community less than do the accidents caused by inadequate visibility.

1.5 Background for design criteria. (1) The criteria for roadway lighting in North America have been based on horizontal illuminance. However, it is known that pavement luminance and veiling luminance (glare) criteria provide a better correlation with the visual impression of roadway lighting quality. It is possible to satisfy illuminance criteria and fall far short of the luminance criteria. Nevertheless, it is also recognized that luminance criteria do not comprise a direct measure of the visibility of features of traffic routes, such as the traffic and fixed hazards on these routes. Unfortunately, certain proposed visibility criteria (see Appendix D) are based on limited research and evaluation and cannot be adopted at this time. For this reason and because luminance criteria do correlate with the visual impression of roadway lighting quality, this Standard Practice gives recommendations for pavement luminance and veiling luminance.

Research has shown that the visual processes permit detection of lower contrasts as the background around those contrasts is raised in luminance. Since the pavement often serves as the background for the detection of objects, it is important to consider the average level of pavement luminance, and its uniformity in roadway lighting design. Pavement luminance is determined by the location of the observer, the quantity of light reaching the pavement, its relative incidence, and the reflection characteristics of the pavement.

(2) Horizontal illuminance is a function only of the amount of light striking various parts of the surface and on the vertical direction of light travel. It is not dependent on the lateral directivity nor on pavement reflectance characteristics, thus variations in luminaire geometry and reflectance characteristics that may cause a wide variation in perceived pavement brightness are not controlled by use of illuminance criteria. On the other hand, illuminance criteria can provide similar visual performance if good design judgment is utilized in application. As a result, even though visual performance cannot be as well controlled by specification, the use of illuminance criteria can be an effective and an equally acceptable alternate.

(3) Since roadway luminance depends upon

pavement reflectance characteristics, observer position and luminaire location and performance, calculations and measurements are more complex than for illuminance. With the development of computer programs, hand calculators, and abbreviated techniques, however, the use of the luminance method is now practical for many roadway lighting agencies.

The IES recognizes that calculation and measurement of pavement luminance will be difficult and burdensome for some agencies. For this reason, the illuminance method has been retained as an alternative design method. It should be noted also that some level of correlation exists between illuminance and luminance depending upon the roadway configuration and the light distribution characteristics of luminaires.

(4) Luminance is the primary and preferred basis of this Standard Practice; but, illuminance criteria are included as an acceptable equal alternative. However, there are two major exceptions where illuminance is presented as the only criteria in this Standard Practice—high mast and walkway/bikeway lighting systems. Both of these cases involve somewhat different design goals than the creation of bright pavements.

(5) The other parameter in roadway lighting that affects visual performance is the glare from the fixed lighting system. The Disability Glare (Veiling Luminance) has been quantified to give the designer information to identify the veiling effect of the glare as a percentage of the average overall luminance. This gives a better means of evaluating the glare from a lighting system than the method (used in conjunction with the illuminance criteria) of merely classifying a single luminaire distribution as to the amount of luminous flux above certain vertical angles.

1.6 Energy management implications. The use of this Standard Practice will result in good lighting and achieve effective energy management if the designer and user will utilize:

(a) Efficient luminaires and lamps for the area to be lighted

(b) A good maintenance program to insure system integrity and to maintain the design level

(c) Appropriate mounting heights and luminaire positioning

1.7 Organization of the Standard Practice. This Standard Practice is divided into the following general subject areas: classifications of areas, pavements, and luminaire light distributions; roadway lighting design; and pedestrian walkway and bikeway lighting design. Supplemental materials of a more detailed and computational nature are included in the appendices. The lighting designer will find the bibliography of Appendix I to be an invaluable, up-to-date reference source on the subject of roadway lighting. For those unfamiliar with the language of lighting and roadway design, Appendix H can be used as a guide to the definition of roadway terms.

2. Classification definitions

2.1 Roadway, pedestrian walkway, and bikeway classifications. (1) *Freeway.* A divided major roadway with full control of access and with no crossings at grade. This definition applies to toll as well as non-toll roads.

(a) *Freeway A:* Roadways with greater visual complexity and high traffic volumes. Usually this type of freeway will be found in major metropolitan areas in or near the central core and will operate through much of the early evening hours of darkness at or near design capacity.

(b) *Freeway B:* All other divided roadways with full control of access where lighting is needed.

(2) *Expressway.* A divided major roadway for through-traffic with partial control of access and generally with interchanges at major crossroads. Expressways for noncommercial traffic within parks and park-like areas are generally known as parkways.

(3) *Major.* That part of the roadway system which serves as the principal network for through-traffic flow. The routes connect areas of principal traffic generation and important rural highways entering the city.

(4) *Collector.* The distributor and collector roadways servicing traffic between major and local roadways. These are roadways used mainly for traffic movements within residential, commercial and industrial areas.

(5) *Local.* Roadways used primarily for direct access to residential, commercial, industrial, or other abutting property. They do not include roadways carrying through traffic. Long local roadways will generally be divided into short sections by collector roadway systems.

(6) *Alley.* Narrow public ways within a block, generally used for vehicular access to the rear of abutting properties.

(7) *Sidewalk.* Paved or otherwise improved areas for pedestrian use, located within public street rights-of-way which also contain roadways for vehicular traffic.

(8) *Pedestrian walkway.* A public walk for pedestrian traffic not necessarily within the right-of-way for a vehicular traffic roadway. Included are skywalks (pedestrian overpasses), subwalks (pedestrian tunnels), walkways giving access to parks or block interiors and midblock street crossings.

(9) *Isolated interchange.* A grade-separated roadway crossing, which is not part of a continuously lighted system, with one or more ramp connections with the crossroad.

(10) *Isolated intersection.* The general area where two or more noncontinuously lighted roadways join or cross at the same level. This area includes the roadway and roadside facilities for traffic movement in that area. A special type is the channelized intersection in which traffic is directed into definite paths by islands with raised curbing.

(11) *Bikeway.* Any road, street, path, or way that is specifically designated as being open to bicycle travel, regardless of whether such facilities are designed for the exclusive use of bicycles or are to be

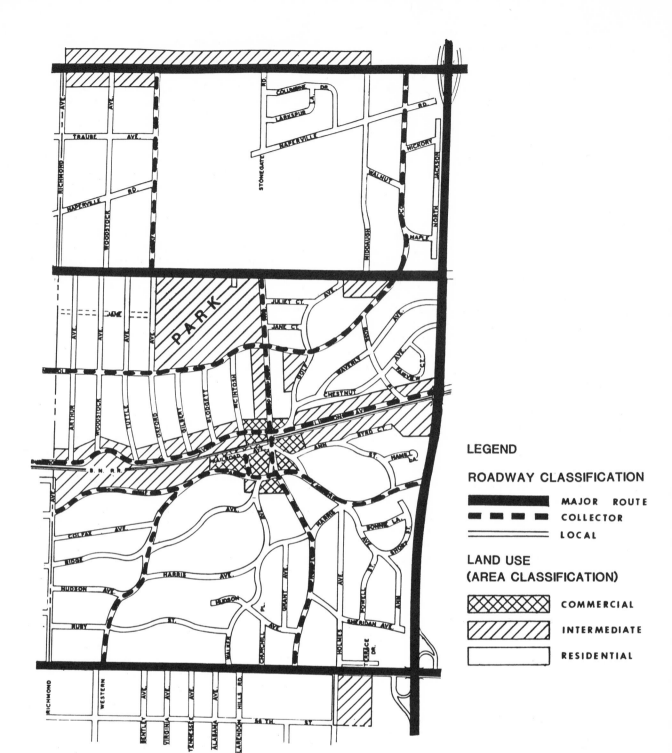

Figure 1. Example of roadway and area classification.

shared with other transportation modes.

(1) *Type A—Designated bicycle lane.* A portion of roadway or shoulder which has been designated for use by bicyclists. It is distinguished from the portion of the roadway for motor vehicle traffic by a paint stripe, curb, or other similar devices.

(2) *Type B—Bicycle trail.* A separate trail or path from which motor vehicles are prohibited and which is for the exclusive use of bicyclists or the shared use of bicyclists and pedestrians. Where such a trail or path forms a part of a highway, it is separated from the roadways for motor vehicle traffic by an open space or barrier.

2.2 Area classifications (abutting land uses).

(1) *Commercial.* A business area of a municipality where ordinarily there are many pedestrians during night hours. This definition applies to densely de-

Table 1. Road surface classifications.

Class	Q_o	Description	Mode of Reflectance
R1	0.10	Portland cement concrete road surface. Asphalt road surface with a minimum of 15 percent of the aggregates composed of artificial brightener (e.g., Synopal) aggregates (e.g., labradorite, quartzite).	Mostly diffuse
R2	0.07	Asphalt road surface with an aggregate composed of a minimum 60 percent gravel (size greater than 10 milimeters). Asphalt road surface with 10 to 15 percent artificial brightener in aggregate mix. (Not normally used in North America.)	Mixed (diffuse and specular)
R3	0.07	Asphalt road surface (regular and carpet seal) with dark aggregates (e.g., trap rock, blast furnace slag); rough texture after some months of use (typical highways).	Slightly specular
R4	0.08	Asphalt road surface with very smooth texture.	Mostly specular

Note: Q_o = representative mean luminance coefficient.

veloped business areas outside, as well as within, the central part of a municipality. The area contains land use which attracts a relatively heavy volume of nighttime vehicular and/or pedestrian traffic on a frequent basis.

(2) *Intermediate.* Those areas of a municipality often characterized by moderately heavy nighttime pedestrian activity such as in blocks having libraries, community recreation centers, large apartment buildings, industrial buildings, or neighborhood retail stores.

(3) *Residential.* A residential development, or a mixture of residential and small commercial establishments, characterized by few pedestrians at night. This definition includes areas with single family homes, town houses, and/or small apartment buildings.

(4) *Certain land uses*, such as office and industrial parks, may fit into any of the above classifications. The classification selected should be consistent with the expected night pedestrian activity.

(5) Figure 1 illustrates use of the roadway and area classification system as applied to a small town.

2.3 Pavement classifications. The calculation of pavement luminance requires information about the surface reflectance characteristics of the pavement.

Studies have shown that most common pavements can be grouped into a limited number of standard road surfaces having specified reflectance data given by r-Tables.

For purposes of this Standard Practice, pavement reflectance characteristics will follow the established CIE* document.[37] A description of pavement classes is given in Table 1. The r-Tables quantifying the pavement classes are in Appendix B4 in Tables B1 through B4.

2.4 Classification of Performance of Luminaire Light Distribution. Proper distribution of the light flux from luminaires is one of the essential factors in efficient roadway lighting. The light emanating from the luminaires is directionally controlled and proportioned in accordance with the roadway width, spacing between luminaires, and the mounting locations where the luminaire is expected to be used. There is, therefore, a need for a luminaire light distribution classification system to aid the user or designer to narrow down the selection of luminaires that might meet the requirements specified for a given roadway system. The system in general use since the 1963 Standard Practice[13] is described in Appendix E. It applies primarily to typical bidirectional roadway luminaires.

3. Roadway lighting design

3.1 Introduction. (1) The lighting system of a specific road section should accommodate the visual needs of night traffic (vehicular and pedestrian) and be expressed in terms clearly understandable by lighting designers, traffic engineers, and highway administrators.

The visual environmental needs along the roadway are described in this Standard Practice in terms of pavement luminance, luminance uniformity and disability veiling glare produced by the system light sources. Table 2(a) provides the recommended luminance design requirements, uniformity and the relationship between average luminance (L_{avg}) and veiling luminance (L_v).

The visual needs along the roadway may also be satisfied by the use of illuminance criteria. Table 2(b) provides the recommended illuminance design requirements, considering the differences in roadway reflectance characteristics. The designer should not expect that lighting systems designed under either criteria will correlate perfectly with each other.

(2) Appendix D includes information for assessing the visibility conditions which also take into consideration the psychophysiological aspects of human vision and the visual process.

(3) The design of a roadway lighting system involves consideration of visibility, economics, es-

---

* Commission International de l'Eclairage

Table 2. Recommended maintained luminance and illuminance values for roadways

(a) Maintained luminance values

Road and Area Classification		Average Luminance L_{avg} (cd/m²)	Luminance Uniformity		Veiling Luminance Ratio (maximum) L_v to L_{avg}
			L_{avg} to L_{min}	L_{max} to L_{min}	
Freeway Class A		0.6	3.5 to 1	6 to 1	0.3 to 1
Freeway Class B		0.4	3.5 to 1	6 to 1	0.3 to 1
Expressway	Commercial	1.0	3 to 1	5 to 1	
	Intermediate	0.8	3 to 1	5 to 1	0.3 to 1
	Residential	0.6	3.5 to 1	6 to 1	
Major	Commercial	1.2	3 to 1	5 to 1	
	Intermediate	0.9	3 to 1	5 to 1	0.3 to 1
	Residential	0.6	3.5 to 1	6 to 1	
Collector	Commercial	0.8	3 to 1	5 to 1	
	Intermediate	0.6	3.5 to 1	6 to 1	0.4 to 1
	Residential	0.4	4 to 1	8 to 1	
Local	Commercial	0.6	6 to 1	10 to 1	
	Intermediate	0.5	6 to 1	10 to 1	0.4 to 1
	Residential	0.3	6 to 1	10 to 1	

(b) Average maintained illuminance values (E_{avg}) in lux

Road and Area Classification		Pavement Classification			Illuminance Uniformity Ratio (E_{avg} to E_{min})
		R1	R2 and R3	R4	
Freeway Class A		6	9	8	3 to 1
Freeway Class B		4	6	5	
Expressway	Commercial	10	14	13	
	Intermediate	8	12	10	3 to 1
	Residential	6	9	8	
Major	Commercial	12	17	15	
	Intermediate	9	13	11	3 to 1
	Residential	6	9	8	
Collector	Commercial	8	12	10	
	Intermediate	6	9	8	4 to 1
	Residential	4	6	5	
Local	Commercial	6	9	8	
	Intermediate	5	7	6	6 to 1
	Residential	3	4	4	

Notes

L_v = veiling luminance

1. These tables do not apply to high mast interchange lighting systems, *e.g.*, mounting heights over 20 meters. See Appendix B5.

2. The relationship between individual and respective luminance and illuminance values is derived from general conditions for dry paving and straight road sections. This relationship does not apply to averages.

3. For divided highways, where the lighting on one roadway may differ from that on the other, calculations should be made on each roadway independently.

4. For freeways, the recommended values apply to both mainline and ramp roadways.

5. The recommended values shown are meaningful only when designed in conjunction with other elements. The most critical elements as described in this practice are:
   (a) Lighting System Depreciation (see paragraph 3.7)
   (b) Quality (see paragraph 3.2)
   (c) Uniformity (see paragraph 3.3)
   (d) Luminaire Mounting Height (see paragraph 3.4)
   (e) Luminaire Spacing (see paragraph 3.5)
   (f) Luminaire Selection (see paragraph 3.6)
   (g) Traffic Conflict Area (see paragraph 3.8)
   (h) Lighting Termination (see paragraph 3.10)
   (i) Alley (see paragraph 3.11)
   (j) Roadway Lighting Layout (see paragraph 3.12)

thetics, safety, and environmental conditions, as well as appropriate material and equipment. The design process follows these major steps:

(a) Determination of roadway classification and abutting land uses along the specific road section to be lighted (Fig. 1). If the pavement classification is unknown, use the R3 values of Table 2.

(b) Selection of the level and uniformity of pavement luminance and assessment of the relationship between the veiling luminance and the average pavement luminance, as recommended in Table 2(a) for each different land use along the section, or

(c) Determination of roadway pavement classification, desired average horizontal levels of illuminance, and uniformity for design as recommended in Table 2(b).

(d) Selection of several tentative luminaires and light sources.

(e) Selection of one or more tentative lighting system geometric arrangements, including mounting heights and lateral luminaire positions, which may provide an acceptable design based on recommended level, uniformity, and/or veiling luminance control.

(f) Calculation of pole spacing for the various luminaire-lamp combinations under study (if for a new system) or of lamp output requirements (if existing poles are to be used), based on illuminance values. Variables of mounting height or lateral luminaire positions may also be considered to verify meeting the requirements of Table 2(a) or 2(b).

(g) When luminaires have been selected, borderline situations quickly become evident during the application stage. In most cases skilled judgment must be exercised when considering luminaires for a specific system. It may not be appropriate to specify only one light distribution when it is obvious that several luminaire light distributions will provide equivalent performance for a specific application.

Table 3. Recommended maintained illuminance design levels for high mast lighting.*†

Road Classification	Horizontal Illuminance (E_{avg}) in Lux		
	Commercial Area	Intermediate Area	Residential Area
Freeways	6	6	6
Expressways	10	8	6
Major	12	9	6
Collector	8	6	6

*Recommended uniformity of illumination is 3 to 1 or better; average-to-minimum for all road classifications at the illuminance levels recommended above.

†These design values apply only to the travelled portions of the roadway. Interchange roadways are treated individually for purposes of uniformity and illuminance level analysis.

Table 4. Recommended average maintained illuminance levels for pedestrian ways* in lux.

Walkway and Bikeway Classification†	Minimum Average Horizontal Levels (E_{avg})	Average Vertical Levels For Special Pedestrian Security (E_{avg})‡
Sidewalks (roadside) and Type A bikeways:		
Commercial areas	10	22
Intermediate areas	6	11
Residential areas	2	5
Walkways distant from roadways and Type B bikeways:		
Walkways, bikeways, and stairways	5	5
Pedestrian tunnels	43	54

*Crosswalks traversing roadways in the middle of long blocks and at street intersections should be provided with additional illumination.

†See Section 2.1.

‡For pedestrian identification at a distance. Values are 1.8 meters above walkway.

(h) Selection of final design or reentry of the design process at any step above to advise on optimal design.

(i) Selection of luminaire supports (pole and bracket) which results in an acceptable esthetic appearance, adherence to traffic safety practice, low initial construction cost, and minimal operation and maintenance expenses.

(j) Recommended illuminance values for high mast lighting are shown in Table 3. For separate walkways or bicycle routes, recommended illuminances are shown in Table 4. The steps to develop optimal design are similar to those given above.

(4) The formation of a tentative design concept involves many variables. The choice of light source, the extent to which available electrical distribution facilities are used, and the types of poles, brackets and luminaires selected are some of the factors that will influence the economics of lighting. Any consideration of appearance is ultimately resolved by professional judgment; however, elaborate or ornate designs, purely for the purpose of satisfying an esthetic desire, cannot be justified unless the basic requirements of good visibility have first been attained. It is important that roadway lighting is planned on the basis of traffic information, which includes the factors necessary to provide for traffic safety and pedestrian security. Some of the factors applicable to the specific problems that should be considered are:

(a) Type of land use development abutting the roadway or walkway (see Section 2.2, "Area Classifications")

(b) Type of route (see Section 2.1, "Roadway, Pedestrian Walkway, and Bikeway Classifications")

(c) Traffic accident experience

(d) Nighttime security needs

(e) Roadway conditions, such as:

(i) Width of pavement and location of curbs adjacent and within the roadway (islands and medians)

(ii) Pavement reflectance

(iii) Severe grades and curves

(iv) Location and width of sidewalks and shoulders

(v) Type and location of very high volume driveways

(vi) Intersections and interchanges

(vii) Underpasses and overpasses

(viii) Trees

3.2 Quality. (1) Quality of lighting relates to the relative ability of the available light to provide the contrast differences so that people can make quick, accurate and comfortable detection, and/or recognition of the cues required for the seeing task. If the quality of lighting of an installation is higher than that of a second installation for the same average luminance level, then visual detection of typical tasks is faster or easier under the first installation.

(2) Many factors are interrelated to produce improved quality of lighting. Although the quantitative values and relative importance of these factors are difficult to specify, the following are involved:

(a) Disability glare and discomfort glare—should be minimized

(b) Reflected specular glare—will conceal some contrast difference

(c) A change in pavement luminance—will change contrast

(d) Uniformity of pavement luminance and other background areas and uniformity of horizontal and vertical illuminance

(3) It should be recognized that in many instances, changes intended to optimize one factor relating to quality will adversely affect another and the resultant total quality of the installation may be degraded. In order to achieve a proper compromise among these factors, this Standard Practice or the Appendices provide definitions and recommendations covering:

(a) Luminaire light distribution in regard to vertical light distribution, lateral light distribution, and vertical control. (see Appendix E.)

(b) Mounting height as a function of maximum candlepower.

(c) Minimum luminance at any point on the roadway as related to average values, as well as maximum/minimum ratios.

(d) Luminare locations as related to roadway elements (see Appendix A).

(4) When designing by the illuminance method, guidance as to typical current practice in mounting heights for a measure of glare control, may be found in Fig. 3.

3.3 Uniformity. (1). Uniformity may be expressed in several ways. The *Average Level-to-Minimum*

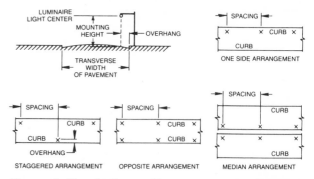

Figure 2. Terminology with respect to luminaire arrangement and spacing.

Point Method uses the average luminance of the roadway design area between two adjacent luminaires, divided by the lowest value at any point in the area. The *Maximum-to-Minimum Point Method* uses the maximum and minimum values between the same adjacent luminaires.

(2) The luminance values provided in Table 2(a) are considered to be satisfactory only if the average-to-minimum and maximum-to-minimum uniformity ratios do not exceed the limits specified in this table (see Appendix B, Section B4). The illuminance values given in Table 2(b) are satisfactory if the average-to-minimum uniformity ratios are not substantially exceeded (see Appendix B, Section B3.4).

(3) A specified luminaire and lamp position provides a distinct light distribution. The same luminaire, utilizing a different type and/or size lamp, or a different lamp position, may provide an entirely different light distribution and uniformity ratio.

(4) The transverse position of a luminaire, the mounting height and tilt all affect the light distribution spread and, hence, its uniformity. These factors must all be considered in relation to the spacing-to-mounting height ratio.

(5) The luminance uniformity (average-to-minimum and maximum-to-minimum) considers the traveled portion of the roadway, except for divided highways having different designs on each side.

Note: A system design must use photometric data for each actual type and make of luminaire and lamp being considered.

3.4 Luminaire mounting height. (1) Mounting heights of luminaires have, in general, increased substantially during the past decade because of the advent of modern, more efficacious, and higher lumen output lamps. Engineers have increased mounting heights in order to obtain economic and esthetic gains in addition to increased uniformity of luminance and illuminance values when utilizing modern lamps. Examples are the 12- to 15-meter and higher mounting heights used along roadways, and the high mast cluster mounting of luminaires at interchanges. The advent of suitable servicing equipment has made this practical.

(2) During this same period there has been a trend to lower mounting heights in some cases. In general, this has been due to esthetic considerations. An example is the use of pole-top-mounted luminaires in residential areas, despite their reduced coefficient of utilization (CU) as related to conventional luminaires that overhang the roadways.

(3) When designing a system, mounting height must be considered in conjunction with spacing and lateral positioning of the luminaires, as well as the luminaire type and distribution. Uniformity and levels of luminance or illuminance must be maintained as recommended, regardless of the mounting height selected.

(4) Increased mounting height will usually (but not necessarily) reduce discomfort glare and disabling veiling luminance. It increases the angle between the luminaires and the line of sight to the roadway; however, luminaire light distribution and candlepower also are significant factors. Glare is dependent on the flux reaching the observer's eyes from all luminaires in the visual scene.

(5) Multi-level interchanges or highway sections with three or four separate roadways may be advantageously lighted with high mast-type units where high intensity sources are suspended in clusters at heights of over 20 meters. Such a design improves traffic safety by reducing the number of poles. High mast units also offer greater flexibility in pole location. (See Section 3.14.)

With the present state-of-the-art, the calculation method of luminance for high mast lighting is questionable. High mast lighting design should be based on illuminance. The method of calculation and high mast system layout principles are outlined in Appendix B, Section B5.

3.5 Luminaire spacing. The spacing of luminaires is often influenced by the location of utility poles, block lengths, property lines, and roadway geometry. It is generally more economical to use lamps with high lumen output at more reasonable spacings and mounting heights than to use lamps with lower lumen output at more frequent intervals with lower mounting heights. Higher mounting is usually in the interests of good lighting, provided the spacing-to-mounting height ratio is within the range of lighting distribution for which the luminaire is designed. The desired ratio of lowest luminance at any point on the pavement to the average luminance value should be maintained. Disregarding luminaire light distribution characteristics and exceeding maximum spacing-to-mounting height ratios can cause loss of visibility of objects between luminaires. Terminology with respect to luminaire arrangement and spacing is shown in Fig. 2.

Optimum luminaire location is best determined by reference to the photometric data showing lighting distribution and utilization. Other factors that must be considered are:

    (*a*) Access to luminaires for servicing
    (*b*) Vehicle-pole collision probabilities
    (*c*) System glare aspects
    (*d*) Visibility (both day and night) of traffic signs and signals
    (*e*) Esthetic appearance

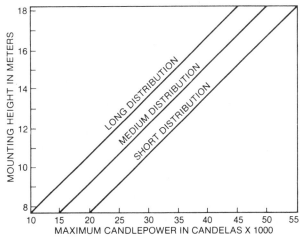

Figure 3. Minimum luminaire mounting heights based on current practice and DVB (Disability Veiling Brightness) calculations.

    (*f*) Trees
    (*g*) Locations of poles at intersections to allow joint use for traffic signals

3.6 Luminaire selection. (1) Luminaire light distribution classifications will help to determine the optical and economical suitability of a luminaire for lighting a particular roadway from the proposed mounting height and mounting location. A wide selection of light distribution systems are available (see Appendix E).

(2) Because a luminaire is assigned a particular classification is no assurance that it will produce the recommended quantity and quality of lighting for all roadway configurations and mountings shown in Fig. 2. The relative amount and control of light in areas other than the cone of maximum candlepower are equally important in producing good visibility in the final system, but are not considered in the classification system.

3.7 Lighting system depreciation. (1) The recommended values of Tables 2, 3, and 4 represent the lowest in-service luminance or illuminance values for the type of maintenance to be given to the system.

Prior to beginning the design of a lighting system it is necessary to determine the expected light losses.

Since the lighting values may depreciate by as much as 50 percent or more between relamping and luminaire cleaning cycles, it is imperative to use lamp lumen depreciation (LLD) and luminaire dirt depreciation (LDD) factors which are based on realistic judgment.

Pavement luminance values also may be changed by wear on the road surface, resulting in modifications of the reflectance coefficient. For example, asphalt tends to lighten due to exposure of aggregate, and Portland cement darkens due to carbon and oil deposits.

(2) There are eight general causes of luminaire light loss (see Appendix B, Section B3.2):
    (*a*) Lamp lumen depreciation (LLD)
    (*b*) Luminaire dirt depreciation (LDD)

(c) Luminaire ambient temperature
(d) Voltage
(e) Ballast and lamp factor
(f) Luminaire component depreciation
(g) Change in physical surroundings
(h) Lamp burning position

Of these eight, the first two represent the major losses recovered periodically. The last six are not usually loss factors to be recovered during normal maintenance procedures. Regardless of recoverability, all eight factors should be considered in design procedures.

(3) One of the principal lighting losses is LLD with in-use aging. Lamp manufacturers provide data showing the light output for average lamps relative to operating time. It is sometimes expressed as mean lumen output during rated life; however, lamp lumen output values used for design purposes should be determined by a thorough study of such data and other lamp operating characteristics. The value selected should be that which occurs at the time of lamp replacement.

Where lamps are to be group replaced (generally the preferable method), the LLD factor should be that which describes the lamp light output at the time of the group replacement interval.

(4) Another major loss is that due to dirt accumulation. The relative luminaire light output remaining after the dirt depreciation has occurred is defined as LDD. It is a function of the type of area, volume of traffic, mounting height, degree of luminaire gasketing, and time since last cleaning. Tests have shown that dirt collection on luminaires along heavily traveled roadways in very dirty atmospheric conditions can reduce light output by 20 percent in a six-month period. Business street luminaires may lose 10 percent in six months, while very clean air at local, residential or outlying highway locations may produce losses of only 5 percent in two years. The maintenance program should be based on measurements of actual local conditions, but frequent cleaning schedules are likely to be justified for luminaires along heavily traveled roadways in dirty areas (see Appendix B, Fig. B2).

3.8 Traffic conflict areas. (1) The values in Table 2 are for roadway sections that are continuous and nearly level. Intersecting, merging or diverging roadway areas may require special consideration. The lighting within these areas should be at least equal to the sum of the values recommended for each roadway that forms the intersection. Very high volume driveway connections to public streets and midblock pedestrian crosswalks should be lighted to at least a 50 percent higher level than the average route value.

(2) Situations involving traffic conflict areas are discussed in Appendix A.

3.9 Roadside areas. (1) From the visibility point of view, there is value in providing lighting in the areas beyond the roadway proper assuming that it is appropriate to the environment and not objectionable to the adjacent property use. It is desirable to widen the narrow visual field into the peripheral zone in order to reveal adjacent objects and enhance eye adaptation. Such conditions also improve depth perception and perspective, thereby facilitating the judgment of speed, distance, etc. The luminance of border areas should diminish gradually and uniformly away from the road.

(2) Roadside, median and interchange infield areas are often attractively landscaped. Both their daytime and nighttime esthetic appearance can often be enhanced by roadway lighting. This should be considered at the time of the lighting system design and when selecting the hardware and street furniture.

3.10 Lighting termination. (1) Transition lighting is a technique intended to provide the driver with a gradual reduction in lighting levels and glare when leaving a lighting system. Some factors that may influence the justification for a transition lighting area are:

(a) Radical reduction in roadway cross section
(b) Severe horizontal or vertical curvature of the roadway
(c) Change from a very high lighting level

It is recommended that the use of transition lighting be at the option of the designer after a study of the conditions at a specific location.

(2) Should transition lighting be used, the techniques for providing a transition are many, and can be applied to all types of lighting systems with varying degrees of complexity.

Decreases in pavement luminance are usually accomplished by extending the lighting system beyond the normal limits, but partially interrupting the required geometric arrangement of luminaires. For example, a two-side opposite or staggered spacing arrangement would continue per design to the normal lighting limits. At this point luminaires would be omitted from the exiting side of the roadway, but continued for one to six cycles beyond the normal limits on the approach side, depending on road speed and luminaire coverage. Generally, with high mast lighting, this can be accomplished with a one-pole installation on the entering side of the lighting system. In this case, it may not require extending the lighting limits as may be needed for lower mounting heights. Designer judgment should be used with various geometric arrangements to effect any transitional change.

3.11 Alleys. Experience indicates that well-lighted alleys may reduce the criminal's opportunity to operate and hide under cover of darkness. It may be desirable to light alleys to facilitate police patrolling from sidewalks and cross streets.

3.12 Roadway lighting layouts. Typical arrangements and spacings of luminaires for several roadway situations are shown in Appendix A. Appendix B provides a guide for calculation of luminance and illuminance levels. It also provides utilization curves, formulas, and typical computations for average candelas per square meter and lux values and at any point on the pavement.

3.13 Partial lighting. (1) Partial lighting refers to a lighting installation with less luminaires than that required for a continuous or complete lighting system. It may consist of a single luminaire only.

(2) Intersections at grade constitute greater traffic conflict due to crossing traffic, turning movements, and changing speeds. With respect to night visibility, such situations require special attention on the part of the driver for safe vehicle operation. For these reasons partial lighting at isolated intersections is sometimes used on unlighted roads.

Partial lighting consisting of one or several luminaires may cause adaptation problems in night driving, particularly when a driver is leaving or entering the lighted area. Therefore, luminaires with glare control should be used.

(3) At low volume intersections a single luminaire is often used for a beacon effect to identify the presence of an intersection.

(4) Appendix A illustrates the suggested locations of the luminaires for various typical situations.

3.14 High mast interchange lighting. (1) High mast interchange lighting is defined as the use of a group of luminaires mounted in excess of 20 meters in height, and is intended to light multiple sections of the paved roadways of an interchange.

(2) The design levels of Table 2 do not apply to high mast interchange lighting systems. The design criteria are given in Table 3. The reason for this is because of a lack of applicable experience in the design of such lighting on a luminance basis. Past experience indicates that a system designed to the illuminance criteria in Table 3 will give satisfactory results.

(3) See Appendix B, Section B5, for the calculation procedure for high mast interchange lighting.

4. Pedestrian walkway and bikeway lighting design

4.1 Introduction. (1) Proper lighting of walkway and bikeway areas is essential to the safe and comfortable use of such areas by pedestrians (herein assumed to include bicyclists) at night. Most walkways and bikeways are located adjacent to lighted roadways and no specific or separate lighting is provided for such pedestrian ways other than the incidental lighting afforded from the house side distribution of roadway luminaires. All too often, such incidental lighting does not produce the proper quality or level for the comfort and safety of pedestrians unless the designer reviews the walkway or bikeway lighting segment and makes modifications to the roadway lighting system to correct any deficiencies.

It is recommended that all preliminary roadway lighting designs be checked for conformance of illuminance requirements prescribed below for pedestrian ways adjacent to roadways, and that revisions and/or additions be made when necessary to achieve proper uniformity.

The photometric data provided by the supplier of the roadway luminaires can be used for checking and designing of sidewalk or roadside bikeway illuminance as well as for roadway illuminance. Where the primary goal of a particular lighting system is to provide adequate illuminance for sidewalks and Type A (roadside) bikeways, initial designs should give greater attention to such pedestrian ways with subsequent checks being made for conformance to roadway lighting requirements.

(2) Lighting walkways and bikeways (Type B) that are not associated with or are substantially distant from roadways permits a greater freedom of system and luminaire design. The designer should exercise good judgment in providing a quality of light that is particularly suitable for these ways and in accordance with recommendations.

4.2 Illuminance requirements. (1) The recommended levels of walkway and bikeway illuminance located in various types of areas are listed in Table 4. These represent average maintained illuminance levels and should be considered as minimum, particularly when security and/or pedestrian identification at a distance is important. Visual identification of other pedestrians and objects along walkways is dependent to a great degree on vertical surface illuminance; therefore, different values are shown in the table.

(2) To provide well-lighted surroundings for such pedestrian ways as walkways and bikeways (Type B) through parks, it is further recommended that the area bordering these pedestrian ways for a width of two to five meters on each side be lighted to levels of at least one-third of that suggested for the walkway or bikeway. This is also applicable to similar marginal areas such as depressed entrances to building basements, gaps between building fronts, dense shrubbery, and other locations where pedestrian safety is of utmost concern.

(3) The average-to-minimum uniformity ratio in illuminating pedestrian ways where special pedestrian security is not essential should not exceed 4 to 1, except for residential sidewalks and Type A bikeways in residential areas, where a ratio of 10 to 1 is acceptable. Where special pedestrian security is deemed desirable, the uniformity ratio should not exceed 5 to 1 for any walkway or bikeway.

(4) The need for good quality lighting that will provide the necessary contrasts and glare-free characteristic in the visual scene is explained in Section 3.2. The designer's selection of mounting height, luminaire spacing, luminaire type and distribution is most important in this regard. Many modern luminaire designs intended for pedestrian ways are now available or are being developed to facilitate individual selection for each installation.

(5) Except for the general overall lighting that may be present in commercial areas, contributions from other nearby storefront lighting, private lighting, sign lighting and/or reflections from structures on private property should not be considered as sufficient reason to reduce the illuminance recommended in this Standard Practice. However, the presence of extensive lines of large trees whose foliage

might interfere with the transmission of light to walkways and bikeways should be considered in establishing design criteria for each location.

4.3 Lighting calculations. Appendix B, Section B6 provides a guide for calculating illuminance levels and uniformity ratios for walkways and bikeways.

Appendix A—Situations requiring special consideration

(This Appendix is not part of the "American National Standard Practice for Roadway Lighting, ANSI/IES RP-8, 1983," but is included for information purposes only.)

A1. Roadway complexities

(1) The design data contained in the "American National Standard Practice for Roadway Lighting" are for straight and level roadway areas and areas having minor curves and grades. Recommendations for safe sight stopping distances are not a part of this Appendix. These are provided in traffic engineering handbooks. Roadways, however, have many areas where the problems of vision and maneuvering of motor vehicles are much more complex, such as grade intersections, abrupt curves, underpasses, converging traffic lanes, diverging traffic lanes and various types of complicated traffic interchanges. The design of roadway lighting for these areas demands special consideration.

(2) When all of these areas are analyzed, it becomes apparent that there are the following three basic factors that are fundamentally different from those encountered on normal straight roadway areas:

(*a*) Motor vehicle operators are burdened with increased visual and mental tasks upon approaching and negotiating these areas.

(*b*) Silhouette seeing cannot be provided in many cases due to the vehicle locations, pedestrian locations, obstructions, and the general geometry of the roadways. Glare from oncoming headlights that sweep across the driver's line of sight is often a problem.

(*c*) Adequate vehicle headlighting often cannot be provided. This is due to the geometry of roadways, lack of stopping room within headlight distances at speeds above 55 kilometers per hour, and the fact that vehicle headlighting follows rather than leads the progress of a vehicle in negotiating turns.

(3) The lighting of such areas, at first glance, appears to be a very complicated problem. It becomes apparent upon analysis, however, that all such areas consist of several basic types of situations or a combination of these. The basic six situations are treated individually in the following sections.

A1.1 Grade intersections, balanced heavy traffic. (See Fig. A1 and A2.) (1) These intersections may

have unrestricted traffic flow on both roadways, restriction by means of stop signs on one or both of the roadways, control by traffic signals, control by police officers or other means. Some are complicated by pedestrian as well as vehicular traffic. The lighting problem on all of these, however, is fundamentally the same. The luminance level in these areas should be higher than the level of either intersecting road. Refer to section 3.8 for appropriate levels.

(2) Luminaires should be located so that lighting will be provided on vehicles and pedestrians in the intersection area, on the pedestrian walkways, and on the adjacent roadway areas (see Fig. A2, a to d). Of particular importance here is the amount of light falling on the vertical surfaces of such objects that differentiates them from the pavement background they are seen against.

(3) Figure A1(b) shows a larger, more complex intersection. The lighting problems and techniques are similar to the small intersections. The size, however, may require the use of more or higher-output luminaires.

A1.2 Curves and hills. (See Fig. A3.) (1) The visual problems in driving increase on curves and hills. In general, gradual, large radius curves and gently sloping grades are lighted satisfactorily if treated as straight level roadway surfaces. Sharper radius curves and steeper grades, especially at the crest of hills, warrant closer spacing of luminaires in order to provide higher pavement luminance and improved uniformities (see Fig. A3, e and f).

(2) The geometry of abrupt curves, such as those found on traffic interchanges (see Fig. A1) and many roadway areas, requires careful analysis. Headlighting is not effective in these situations and silhouette seeing cannot be provided in some instances. Luminaires should be located to provide ample light on vehicles, road curbings and berms, guard rails, etc. Poles should be located to provide adequate, safe clearance, behind guardrail or any natural barrier if such exists. There is some evidence that poles are more likely to be involved in accidents if placed on the outside of curves. Many vehicle operators may be unfamiliar with these areas and lighting the surroundings greatly helps their discernment of the roadway path (see Fig. A3, c and d).

(3) Proper horizontal orientation of luminaire supports and poles on curves is important to assure balanced distribution of the light flux on the pavement (see Fig. A3(a)).

(4) When luminaires are located on steep grades, it is desirable to orient the luminaire so that the light beams strike the pavement equidistant from the luminaire. This assures maximum uniformity of light distribution and keeps glare to a minimum (see Fig. A3(b)).

A1.3 Underpasses and overpasses (see Fig. A1). (1) Short underpasses such as those encountered where a roadway goes beneath a two- or four-lane roadway can generally be lighted satisfactorily with standard luminaires if they are properly positioned.

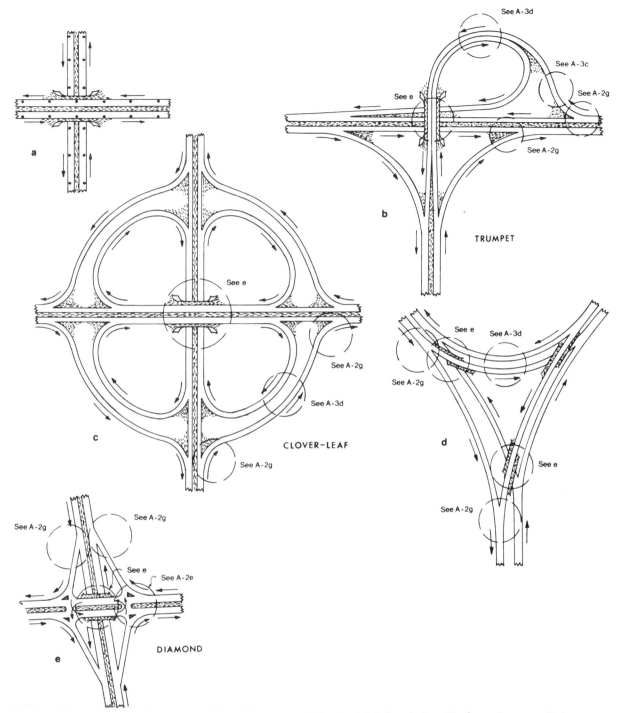

Figure A1. Roadway complexities: (a) underpass-overpass; and (b) to (e) traffic interchanges. Note: arrows indicate traffic flow directions. Pole location will depend on local practice and physical conditions of the area.

Luminaires on the lower roadway should be positioned so that there are not large discontinuities in the pavement lighting from that on either side of the overpass and so that the recommended levels are provided. Care should be taken so that the uniformity does not fall below the minimum values recommended in Table 2. These luminaires should also provide adequate vertical illumination on the supporting structures.

(2) Long underpasses, where such overlapping of

the lighting from the street luminaires cannot be accomplished, require special treatment. Long underpasses also greatly reduce the entrance of daylight, warranting lighting during the daytime. This is justified to very high luminance levels. For further information of the lighting of long tunnels and underpasses, see Appendix I (Bibliography), references 22, 23, 69, 83, 98, 106 and 109.

A1.4 Converging traffic lanes. (See Fig. A2.)

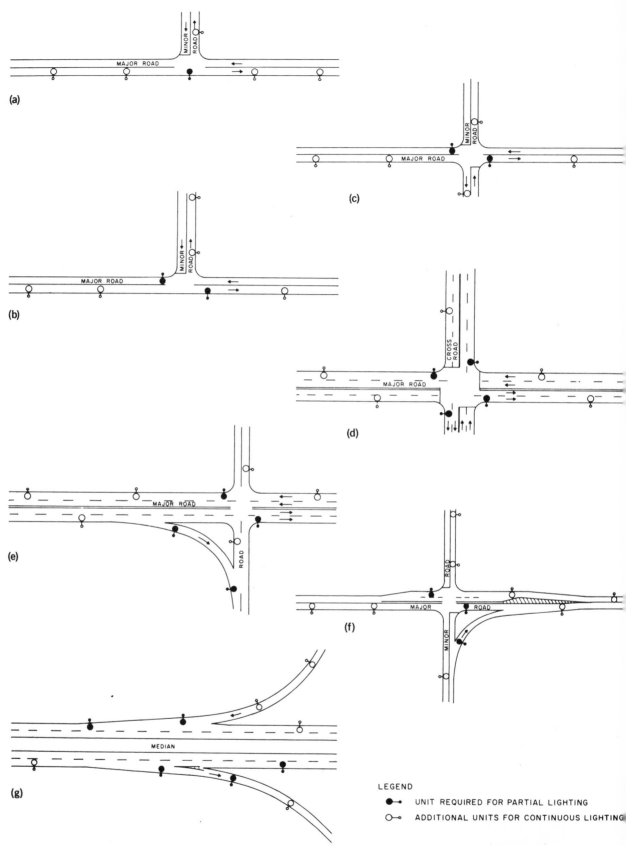

Figure A2. Location of luminaires to provide illumination on vehicles and pedestrians in the intersection area, on the pedestrian walkways, and on the adjacent roadway areas for: (a) T-intersection; (b) T-intersection (alternate); (c) four-way intersection, two-lane road with two-lane sideroad; (d) signalized intersection, four-lane road with four-lane crossroad; (e) four-lane road with channelizing island; (f) intersection with channelizing island; and (g) typical acceleration and deceleration lanes at on and off ramps. Note: Figures are not to scale and light locations shown are not to be considered complete in number or better than approximate in location.

LEGEND

●—○ UNIT REQUIRED FOR PARTIAL LIGHTING
○—○ ADDITIONAL UNITS FOR CONTINUOUS LIGHTING

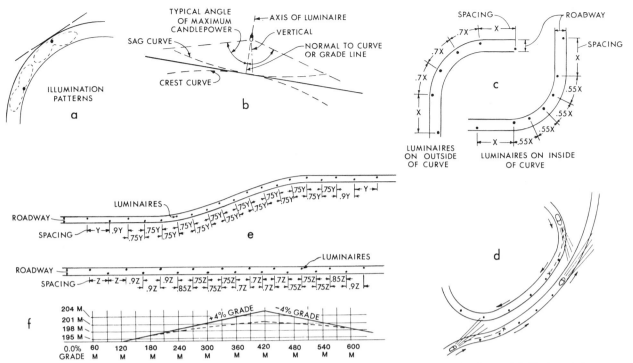

Figure A3. Typical lighting layouts for horizontal curves and vertical curves. (a) Luminaires oriented to place reference plane perpendicular to radius of curvature. (b) Luminaire mounting on hill (vertical curves and grade). (c) Short radius curves (horizontal). (d) Vehicle illumination limitations. **(e) Horizontal curve, radius 305 meters, super elevation 6% per foot. (f) 380-meter vertical curve with four per cent grade and 230-meter sight distance.**

Converging traffic lanes frequently have all the problems of abrupt curves. Here, vehicle headlighting is ineffective and silhouette seeing cannot be provided for many of the situations. It is also essential to provide good direct side lighting on the vehicles entering the main traffic lanes. Refer to Section 3.8 for proper levels.

A1.5 Diverging traffic lanes. (See Fig. A2.) Diverging traffic lanes warrant extremely careful consideration because these are areas where motorists are most frequently confused. Luminaires should be placed to provide illumination on curbs, abutments, guard rails, and vehicles in the area of traffic divergence. Poles should be located to provide adequate safety clearance for vehicles that may cross the gore area. Lighting also should be provided in the deceleration zone. Diverging roadways frequently have all the problems of abrupt curves and should be treated accordingly. Refer to Section 3.8 for proper levels.

A1.6 Interchanges (high-speed, high-traffic-density roadways). (See Fig. A1, and Fig. A2.) **(1)** At first glance, interchanges appear to be complex lighting problems. However, analysis shows that they are comprised of one or more of the basic problems that are dealt with in previous paragraphs and may be treated accordingly.

(2) The regular roadway lighting system will usually provide sufficient surrounding illuminance to reveal the features of the entire scene so that drivers will know where they are and where they are going at all times. An inadequately lighted interchange with too few luminaires may lead to confusion for the driver, by giving misleading clues due to the random placement of the luminaires. (This does not apply to high mast lighting).

(3) When continuous lighting of the entire interchange area cannot be provided, it may be desirable to light intersections, points of access and egress, curves, hills and similar areas of geometric and traffic complexity. In these cases, lighting should be extended beyond the critical areas. Two fundamental reasons for this are:

(a) The eyes of the driver, adapted to the level of the lighted area, need about one second to adjust to changes in the illumination upon leaving the lighted area to maintain vision during the period of dark adaptation. There is no evidence that a gradual reduction at the levels used in roadway lighting has any practical advantage over a sudden ending of the lighted area. This end, however, should be beyond the end of the maneuver area.

(b) Traffic merging into a major roadway from an access road is often slow in accelerating to the speed on the major roadway. The lighting along this area for a distance beyond the access point extends visibility and facilitates the acceleration and merging process.

(4) The placement of luminaires should be carefully considered to minimize glare to the drivers and especially so as to not detract from sign legibility or to block the view of signs.

A2. Railroad grade crossings

(1) Railroad grade crossings should be adequately lighted to identify the crossing, any irregularities in the pavement surface, the presence or absence of a train in or approaching the crossing, and to allow recognition of unlighted objects or vehicles at or near the railroad crossing.

(2) Grade crossings are normally identified by means of identification signs with the message on a vertical face, and/or markings on the pavement surface. Lighting direction and level should permit visual recognition of such signs and markings. Minor variation of the basic lighting layouts shown in Fig. A4 may be desirable, depending on the exact locations of such signs or markings.

(3) General principles to be followed in selecting and locating equipment are as follows:

(*a*) Luminance level over track area, starting 30 meters before the crossing and ending 30 meters beyond the crossing, should be in accordance with Table 2, but never less than a luminance of 0.8 candelas per square meter or an illuminance of 8 lux (see Fig. A4a).

(*b*) Pole location should provide (Fig. A4, b through e) uniformity in accordance with Section 3.3.

(*c*) Vertical illumination of a train in the crossing is important for adequate visibility. However, care must be used in locating the luminaire so that glare is not a problem to the drivers approaching the crossings from the opposite direction.

(*d*) Light of a cautionary color may be used; however, distinctive color sources, for effectiveness, depend upon observer recognition of the meaning of that color. There is no evidence that such distinctive colors have any practical advantage.

A3. Trees

(1) Both trees and roadway lighting are indispensable municipal assets. Through understanding and cooperation of those responsible, trees and roadway lighting need not conflict.

(2) Arborists should make tree selections based on those that will fit the available roadway space, with minimum conflict to utilities. Such selections may include upright, globular or ordinary tree shapes. In most cases, proper pruning of trees will solve any conflict between trees and roadway lighting.

(3) The presence of low overhanging foliage may seriously obstruct the light delivered to the pavement as well as impede truck movement. Judicious pruning can reduce or eliminate the screening effect. There are instances where pruning increased the average lighting effectiveness approximately one-third, and approximately doubled the lighting effectiveness in the critical areas of low visibility.

(4) It should be noted that even with high-mounted luminaires, it is not necessary to prune all trees to the height of the luminaire. It is necessary to prune only those branches that fall below the useful beam. (see Fig. A5.) Foliage midway between luminaires and somewhat below lamp level helps to screen distant sources where silhouette lighting is intended; the attendant reduction in glare helps visibility and comfort of motorists and pedestrians. This gain is

Figure A4. Railroad grade crossings.

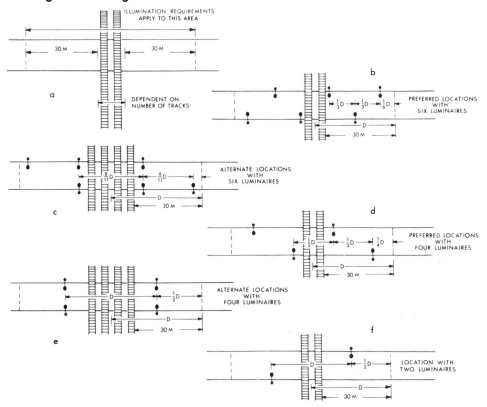

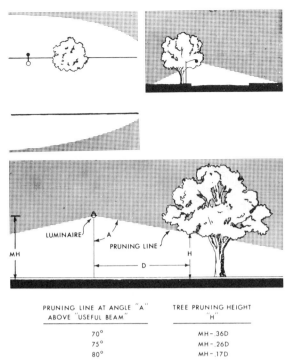

PRUNING LINE AT ANGLE "A" ABOVE "USEFUL BEAM"	TREE PRUNING HEIGHT "H"
70°	MH − .36D
75°	MH − .26D
80°	MH − .17D

Figure A5. Recomended tree pruning to minimize conflict with roadway lighting.

particularly important on local traffic and residential roadways where limited funds usually require relatively long spacings, with correspondingly high candlepower at angles near the horizontal.

(5) Another gain comes from reflection of upward light by the foliage, downward to the roadway and sidewalk. Although the amount is small, it adds to the low illuminance levels on local traffic roadways and increases the general adaptation level.

A3.1 Design compromises. In order to minimize conflicts with trees, there are certain compromises that can be made in the lighting system. These compromises involve deviations from preferred system layouts with respect to luminaire spacing, mounting height, and transverse location. Such deviations usually should be accompanied by modifications in the light distribution provided by the luminaire. The amount of reduction in lighting effectiveness will vary depending upon the circumstances, type of modification and the extent of the deviation.

A3.2 Design modifications. (1) As an example of modification, all luminaires may be mounted on longer mast arms. This generally increases construction costs to some extent, but the gain in lighting effectiveness may be substantial if foliage interference is reduced. Another modification is span-wire suspension of luminaires over the center of the street. Construction costs are substantially higher because two poles are required for each luminaire. A major disadvantage of span-wire suspension is that swaying and bobbing of luminaires in the wind nullifies to a great extent the effectiveness of the light control provided by modern luminaires.

(2) Still another modification is to reduce the luminaire mounting height with a corresponding reduction in spacing, use a lamp of lower lumen output, and lower the angle of maximum candlepower. This method materially increases the cost of roadway lighting.

(3) Only as a last resort, it might be expedient to increase lamp lumen output to compensate for reduction in illuminance levels caused by foliage interference. However, this has serious disadvantages because the impairment of light distribution, increased glare, and uniformity of illumination cannot be corrected by merely increasing lamp sizes. Also, cost will be increased considerably.

A3.3 Design departures. (1) Where deviations in longitudinal spacing of luminaires are made to minimize conflicts with trees, generally a 10 percent deviation from average spacing will not seriously affect the uniformity of lighting. As a maximum compromise for certain types of luminaires, deviations up to 20 percent can be tolerated providing no two consecutive luminaire locations are involved. The variation in pavement luminance should be checked in the design process. When two or more consecutive locations necessitate deviations from the average spacing, then the resulting design should be reanalyzed and perhaps the transverse location or mounting height changed.

(2) Alignment of luminaires out over the street is important in respect to both visibility and appearance. Only where there is no other reasonable compromise should any transverse deviation of an individual luminaire be permitted. The length of the luminaire support should be selected which best meets the requirement of each particular street. It should be kept in mind that when using longer supports that approach the center of the street, pruning requirements become less, but structural costs of installation will increase.

A3.4 Design data. (1) Figs. A6 and A7 are intended to serve as a guide for determining proper overhang

Figure A6. Height to foliage interference for different types of trees and luminaire overhange from curve. (Tree examples by E. H. Scanlon.)

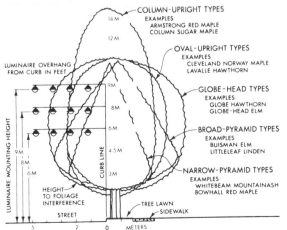

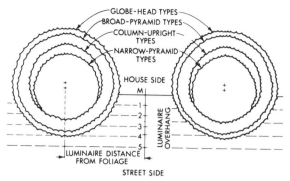

Figure A7. Longitudinal and transverse location of luminaires as related to different types of trees.

distances of luminaires for different heights of mounting and for different types of trees.

(2) Although foliage interference mostly affects the illuminance on the roadway pavement, the importance · of adequate lighting for the sidewalks should not be overlooked. There may be instances on local traffic residential roadways where good sidewalk illumination is even more important than lighting of the roadway itself. Generally, this can be obtained either by altering the luminaire positions or by pruning, or a combination of both methods.

(3) The modern trend in roadway lighting practice is to use light sources of higher efficacy in luminaires having light distributions appropriate for the luminaire spacing, mounting height, and transverse positions, and for the roadway dimensions. Such proper lighting design is particularly important on residential and local streets. Also, it should be emphasized that, where we see by silhouette discernment, the high angle emission of light from the luminaire is very important. Obviously with longer spacings there are proportionately fewer luminaires which, in turn, reduce the requirements for pruning. This further contributes to lower combined maintenance cost of trees and lighting. Observations in different sizes of towns with properly designed roadway lighting indicate that as an average the number of actual conflicts between luminaires and foliage is in the order of 50 percent on the more heavily wooded roadways. It is quite probable that, of the total existing residential and traffic roadway mileage, the foliage interference is considerably less than 50 percent.

Appendix B—Computational method (illuminance and luminance)*

(This Appendix is not part of the "American National Standard Practice for Roadway Lighting," ANSI/IES RP-8, 1983, but is included for information purposes only.)

---

* Most angular symbols are those of CIE (*Commission Internationale de l'Eclairage*) and not those of IES.

B1. Introduction

The basic computations that follow apply to conventional roadway lighting systems mounted alongside the street or highway at heights of 5 to 20 meters above the pavement. Obviously the data and techniques can also be applied to adjacent walkways, median strips and other areas. Horizontal illuminance and lumen depreciation will be discussed in Section B3. Section B4 describes the procedure for computation of luminance. For special computations relating to area lighting with high mast equipment, refer to Section B5. Walkways and bikeways are covered in Section B6.

B2. Lighting calculation principles

(1) The recommended design values, as well as uniformity ratios, are given in Tables 2, 3, and 4. These represent the lowest maintained values that are currently considered appropriate for the kinds of roadways or walkways in various areas. Numerous installations have been made at higher values. Furthermore, the recommendations assume the use of applicable types of luminaire light distribution, lamp sizes, mounting heights, spacings, and transverse locations. These figures do not represent initial readings but should be the *lowest in-service values* of systems designed with the proper light loss factors.

(2) The quantity of light can be described in two different ways:

(*a*) as density of visible energy falling on the surface of the planes or objects; and

(*b*) as the luminous intensity reflecting off such surfaces or objects toward the observer.

The first description of light-quantity involves the incident light that reaches the objects and planes from one or more sources.

For a point source, the luminous intensity (I measured in candelas) in a given direction can be expressed as follows:

$$I = \frac{d\Phi}{d\omega}$$

where

$d\Phi$ = the flux of visible radiation contained in the solid angle $d\omega$ around the line of given direction.

The luminous flux will illuminate the surface of a level equal to:

$$E = \frac{d\Phi}{dA}$$

where

$d\Phi$ = the incident luminous flux

dA = the area.

The unit of measurement of illuminance (E) is the lux, equal to one lumen per square meter.

When the light beam strikes a surface at an angle, the same flux will be distributed over a larger area as compared to when the surface is perpendicular to the beam. As a result the light density will be reduced. The value of the horizontal level of illuminance (E_h) when the intensity of flux (I), the angle of incidence

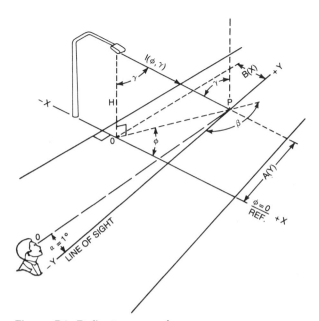

Figure B1. Reflectance angles.

(γ), and the distance (D) from the source are known, can be expressed as follows:

$$E_h = \frac{I \times \cos\gamma}{D^2}$$

The surface luminance (L) is defined as the luminous flux per steradian emitted (reflected) by a unit area of surface in the direction of an observer. When the unit of flux per steradian is candela and the area is measured in square meters, the unit of luminance is candela per square meter. The surface luminance in general terms can be calculated if the reflectance coefficient (q) and the illuminance value is known:

$$L = \frac{1}{\pi^*} E_h \times q(\beta, \gamma)$$

where
  $q(\beta, \gamma)$ = directional reflectance coefficient for angles of incidence of β and γ. (see Fig. B1.)

Although a simple concept of the quantity of light reflected by a surface is assessed from the reflectance coefficient $q(\beta, \gamma)$ the distribution pattern will depend upon the surface characteristics and the angular relationship between the light source, the observation point, and the observer's position.

In principle, two types of reflectance are identified: diffuse and specular (or mirror). Snow is an example of a diffuse surface, whereas a smooth, wet road is a good example of a specular surface. Most road surfaces are a mixture of both diffuse and specular reflectance.

The horizontal illuminance can be expressed as follows:

$$E_h = \frac{I(\phi, \gamma) \times \cos\gamma}{D^2}$$

and

$$D^2 = \frac{H^2}{\cos^2\gamma}$$

where
  H = mounting height
By substituting the D^2 value:

$$E_h = \frac{I(\phi, \gamma) \cos^3\gamma}{H^2}$$

and

$$L = \frac{1}{\pi^*} q(\beta, \gamma)E_h$$

The luminance L then can be written as follows:

$$L = \frac{1}{\pi^*} \frac{q(\beta, \gamma) \times I(\phi, \gamma) \times \cos^3\gamma}{H^2}$$

In practice $q(\beta, \gamma) \cos^3\gamma$ can be expressed as a reduced luminance coefficient r and is given in a table for each road classification (see Tables B1 and B4).** A simplified expression for L can be written as follows:

$$L = \frac{1}{\pi^*} \frac{r(\beta, \gamma) \times I(\phi, \gamma)}{10,000 \, H^2}$$

where $r(\beta, \gamma) = q(\beta, \gamma) \cos^3\gamma$, and β, γ and ϕ are as shown in Fig. B1.

The luminance of a point P can be written as a sum of contributions from all luminaires (n):

$$L_p = \sum_{i=1}^{n} \frac{r(\beta_i, \gamma_i) \times I(\phi_i, \gamma_i)}{\pi^* \, 10,000 \, H^2}$$

The values of I must be depreciated by the light loss factor plus any equipment factors.

B3. Calculation procedure for horizontal illuminance

The general procedure for calculating maintained roadway illuminance consists of a series of steps before the actual calculations begin. These steps are divided into two major groups: (1) objectives and specifications; and (2) the light loss factors. A third group covers the calculations and will vary in the number and type of steps depending on the illuminance desired—average or at a point. The following paragraphs show the steps for calculating maintained levels of illuminance, and the lowest level of illuminance on the roadway.

B3.1 Objectives and specifications. (See Section 2 of the Standard Practice.)

B3.1.1 Quality required. A knowledge and understanding of the quality of illumination required for seeing on roadways is important. (See Section 3.2 in the Standard Practice.)

B3.1.2 Quantity required. The average maintained levels of illuminance to be utilized, or as a reference level to initiate luminance calculations, can be found in Table 2(b), based on the determination of roadway and area classification in Section 2. Also, consideration should be given to allowable limits of uniformity.

---

* π is omitted when area is in square feet, illuminance is in footcandles and luminance is in footlamberts.
** Note that r values in Tables B1 to B4 have been multiplied by 10,000; therefore, the equations that follow have 10,000 in the denominatcr.

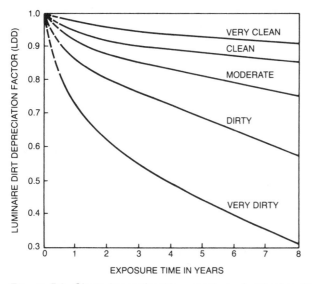

Figure B2. Chart for estimating roadway luminaire dirt depreciation factors for enclosed and gasketed luminaires.

B3.1.3 Area atmosphere. The two main ambient atmospheric contaminations are those generated on the roadway itself (the surrounding atmosphere) and that which is generated from the adjacent atmosphere. Figure B2 shows five groups of typical area atmospheres.

B3.1.4 Route characteristics. A survey and base drawing showing the physical characteristics such as roadway width, curvatures, grade, driveways, and border areas is required.

B3.1.5 Selection of luminaire. Selection of the type of luminaire for a given roadway depends upon dimensions of roadway, mounting height, luminaire dirt depreciation, lamp choice, maintenance consideration (including cleaning and lamp replacement), luminaire and installation appearance, color of light, cost of equipment, etc. All factors, whose relative importance will vary from project to project, should be examined in detail first, then reviewed so that proper weights will be given to each one.

B3.2 Light loss factors (LLF). Once the basic values discussed in B3.1 are established and a preliminary choice of a luminaire is made, light loss factors (LLF) can be studied. Several of these factors—known collectively as the maintenance factor (MF)—are the result of time-dependent depreciation effects. Others—equipment factors (EF)—will exist initially and continue through the life of the installation. However, all factors should be studied and reduced to the extent possible, because they will diminish the planned output of the lighting system.

B3.2.1 Maintenance factors (MF). The result of time-dependent depreciation effects must be considered in the initial design. Regular maintenance is particularly important with regard to energy conservation and these plans, once incorporated into the design, should be carried out or the system will not perform as expected.

B3.2.1.1 Lamp lumen depreciation (LLD). Information about the chosen lamp and its lumen depreciation and mortality are available from lamp manufacturers' tables and graphs. Rated average life should be determined for the specific hours per start; it should be known when burnouts will occur in the lamp life cycle. A typical roadway lighting system will be in operation about 4,000 hours per year. From these facts, a practical group relamping cycle should be established and then, based on the hours elapsed to lamp removal, the specific LLD factor can be determined. Consult manufacturers' data or the latest *IES Lighting Handbook* for LLD factors.[1,2]

B3.2.1.2 Luminaire dirt depreciation (LDD). The accumulation of dirt on luminaires results in a loss in light output on the roadway. this loss is known as the LDD factor and is determined by estimating the dirt category (very clean, clean, moderate, dirty, or very dirty) from definitions given in Fig. B2. From the appropriate dirt condition curve in Fig. B2 and the proper elapsed time in years of the planned cleaning cycle, the LDD factor is then found.

B3.2.1.3 Burnouts. Unreplaced burned-out lamps will vary in quantity, depending on the kinds of lamps and the relamping program used. Manufacturers' lamp mortality statistics should be consulted for the performance of each lamp type so that the number of burn-outs can be determined before the time of planned replacement is reached. Practically, the quantity of lamp burnouts is determined by the quality of the lighting services program and by the physical performance of the program.

B3.2.2 Equipment factors. Light loss factors that are not dependent on time relate mostly to the specific equipment selected, and they are usually of such little effect as to make correction impractical or too costly. However, they can diminish the total light output of the system and should be minimized to the extent possible.

B3.2.2.1 Ambient temperature. The effect of ambient temperature on the output of some lamps may be considerable. Each particular lamp-luminaire combination has its own distinctive characteristic of light output versus ambient temperature. To apply a factor for light loss due to ambient temperature, the designer must know the highest and lowest temperatures expected and to have data showing variations in light output with changes in ambient temperature for the specific lamp to be used.

B3.2.2.2 Voltage. In-service voltage is difficult to predict, but high or low voltage at the luminaire will affect the light output of most lamps.

B3.2.2.3 Ballast and lamp factor.[31] If the ballast factor of the ballast used in a luminaire (fluorescent or high intensity discharge) differs from that of the ballast used in the actual photometry of the luminaire, the light output will differ by the same amount. The manufacturer should be consulted for necessary factors.

B3.2.2.4 Luminaire component depreciation. (1) Surface depreciation results from adverse changes in metal, paint, and plastic components which result in reduced light output.

(2) Because of the complex relationship between the light controlling elements of luminaires using more than one type of material it is difficult to predict losses due to deterioration of materials. Also for various luminaire surfaces, the losses will be differentially affected by the type of atmosphere to which they are exposed. No factors are available at present.

B3.2.2.5 Change in physical surroundings. The designer should know as much as possible about future changes that may affect roadway conditions. In the design process, it is desirable to know when the pavement is in poor condition and if it is likely to be resurfaced early in the useful life of the lighting system. Consideration may also be given as to whether trees or border areas will be added, or nearby buildings constructed or demolished.

B3.3 Total light loss factor. The total light loss factor is obtained by multiplying all the contributing factors described above. Where factors are not known, or believed to be reasonably small, they are omitted. Otherwise, they are estimated based on past experience at similar locations. In all cases, a light loss factor should be used that at least considers the LLD and the LDD. At this point, if it is found that the total light loss factor is excessive it may be desirable to reselect the luminaire and/or lamp, or modify the cleaning and/or maintenance schedule.

B3.4 Calculations. Roadway illuminance calculations fall into three general types: (1) the determination of the average illuminance on the roadway pavement; (2) the illuminance at a specific point on the roadway; and (3) the uniformity of illuminance.

Calculations[32] are based on luminaire photometric data curves that have been published in two formats. One method presents the data based on "per 1000 lamp lumens," and the other method is based on "rated initial lamp lumens."

B3.5 Determination of average illuminance

B3.5.1 General. The average illuminance over a large pavement area may be calculated by means of a "utilization curve," or by computing the illuminance at a large number of specific points and averaging the values found. The utilization curve is a part of the data presented as a result of following the "IES Approved Method for Photometric Testing of Roadway Luminaires." [28]

B3.5.2 Utilization curves. (1) Utilization curves, available for various types of luminaires, afford a practical method to determine average illuminance over the roadway surface where lamp lumen output, mounting heights, width of paved area, and spacing between luminaires are known or assumed. Conversely, the desired spacing or any other unknown factor may readily be determined if the other factors are given.

(2) Fig. B3 is an example of a utilization curve of a typical luminaire. Some manufacturers have combined the utilization curve with the isolux curve (See Fig. B10) and present both sets of curves on the same figure. The utilization curve indicates how much light falls on the roadway, but reveals little of the way in which the light is distributed. Therefore, it should be used in conjunction with the isolux curve in order to evaluate the true performance of the luminaire, especially concerning compliance with the recommended uniformity ratios.

The total coefficient of utilization (CU) is the percentage of rated lamp lumens utilized in lighting

Figure B3. Example of CU (Coefficient of Utilization) curves for luminaire providing medium semicutoff, Type II light distribution.

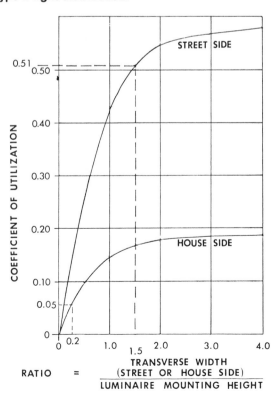

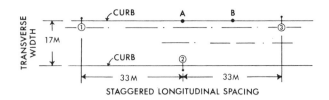

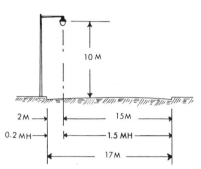

Figure B4. Layout of luminaire and roadway assumed for typical computation.

an area of given width and infinite length. The curves indicate the percentage of flux falling on the area in front of the luminaire (street side) and behind the luminaire (house side). Both areas are strip-like, of infinite length, with widths expressed as a ratio of width to mounting height. To obtain the total utilization for a given area, the CU for both the street and the house side areas must be determined from the curves and added. The luminaire is considered mounted as tested (level) and oriented over the reference line which divides the street side from the house side.

(3) To illustrate the use of a utilization curve, a typical calculation is provided as follows:*

Given: Roadway with layout as shown in Fig. B4.

Staggered luminaire spacing	33 meters
Roadway width curb-to-curb	17 meters
Luminaire mounting height	10 meters
Luminaire overhang	2 meters
Luminaire dirt depreciation factor	0.70
Lamp (rated initial 20,000 lumens)	
Lamp lumen depreciation factor	0.85

Required: To calculate the minimum average illuminance (in lux) for the above roadway.

Solution (for average illuminance):

(*a*) Determine the coefficient of utilization for the "street side" of the luminaire.

Ratio (street side) from Fig. B3:

$$\frac{17 \text{ meters} - 2 \text{ meters}}{10 \text{ meters}} = \frac{15 \text{ meters}}{10 \text{ meters}} = 1.5$$

Coefficient of utilization from Fig. B3 for ratio 1.50 is 0.51

(*b*) Determine coefficient of utilization for the "house side"

Ratio (house side) from Fig. B3:

$$\frac{2 \text{ meters}}{10 \text{ meters}} = 0.2$$

* For conversion from SI values see Appendix G.

Coefficient of utilization from Fig. B3 for ratio 0.2 is 0.05.

(*c*) Total coefficient for "street side" plus "house side" is 0.56

B3.5.3 Formulas for computation. The basic formula for determination of average initial horizontal illuminance is as follows:

Average Initial Illuminance

$$= \frac{(\text{Lamp Lumens}) \times (\text{Coefficient of Utilization})}{(\text{Spacing Between Luminaires}) \times (\text{Width of Roadway})}$$

A further modification of this formula is necessary to determine the average maintained illuminance on the roadway. For this calculation, which is indicative of the illuminance on the pavement when the illuminating source is at its lowest output and the luminaire is in its dirtiest condition, the formula is expressed as follows:

Average Maintained Illuminance

$$= \frac{(\text{Lamp Lumens}) \times (\text{Coefficient of Utilization}) \times (\text{Light Loss Factor})}{(\text{Spacing Between Luminaires}) \times (\text{Width of Roadway})}$$

The spacing between luminaires is the longitudinal distance between luminaires if spaced in staggered or one-sided arrangement. This distance is one-half the longitudinal distance between luminaires if luminaires are arranged in opposite spacing.

To determine the average illuminance on the roadway and at the spacing shown on Fig. B4, assuming a 20,000-lumen lamp in the luminaire from which Fig. B3 was prepared, the following calculation is made:

Average Illuminance

$$= \frac{(20000) \ (0.56) \ (0.70) \ (0.85)}{(33) \ (17)} = 11.9 \text{ lux}$$

If the street is a major route having R1 pavement and adjacent commercial land use (See Section 2), the recommended illuminance value of 12 lux from Table 2(b) may be considered as met (fractions of a lux should be rounded to the nearest whole lux). However, it is also necessary to check whether the uniformity ratio of 3 to 1 is met as specified in Table 2(b). To do this, the illuminance at the lowest point on the roadway must be calculated.

B3.6 Determination of the illuminance at a specific point

B3.6.1 General. The horizontal illuminance in lux at a specific point may be determined from an "isolux" curve (Fig. B5) or by means of the inverse square method of calculation (see the latest edition of the *IES Lighting Handbook*. Since the "Isolux" curve follows the "IES Approved Method for Photometric Testing of Roadway Luminaires,"[28] this method will be discussed.

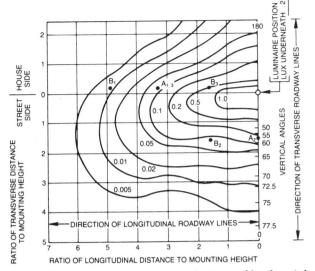

Figure B5. Example of an isolux diagram of horizontal lux on pavement surfaces for a luminaire providing a medium semicutoff, Type II light distribution (per 1000 initial lamp lumens). The isolux data are based on a luminaire mounting height of 9 meters. For other mounting heights, multiply the values of isolux shown by the factors below.

Mounting Height	8	9	10	11	12	13	14	15
Factor	1.27	1.00	0.81	0.87	0.58	0.48	0.41	0.38

B3.6.2 Isolux diagram. (1) An isolux diagram is a graphical representation of points of equal illuminance connected by a continuous line. These lines may show lux values on a horizontal plane from a single unit having a definite mounting height, or they may show a composite picture of the illuminance from a number of sources arranged in any manner or at any mounting height. They are useful in the determination of the level of illuminance at any specific point. In order to make these curves applicable to all conditions, they are computed for a given mounting height but horizontal distances are expressed in ratios of the actual distance to the mounting height. Correction factors for other mounting heights are usually given in the tabulation alongside the curves.

(2) To use the typical isolux diagram, the point on the pavement is located with respect to each luminaire in the system and the dimensions are determined in transverse and longitudinal multiples of the mounting height. The point is located on the isolux diagram (Fig. B5) for each position it assumes with respect to a luminaire. The value of lux contributed by that luminaire is then estimated. If the isolux diagram is of the format based on "per 1000 lamp lumens," the total illuminance value must be multiplied by the ratio:

$$\frac{\text{Rated Lamp Lumens}}{1000}$$

The total contribution from at least the three nearest luminaires should be added to obtain the total illuminance at a point.

(3) To express the illuminance of the point in terms of maintained illuminance, multiply the initial value by the light loss factor.

(4) An illustration of the calculation is given below, utilizing the layout shown on Fig. B4, the roadway and depreciation factors as used for the utilization curve and average lux examples, and Fig B5:

Required: To determine the illuminance at point "A," which is the total of contributions from luminaires 1, 2 and 3.

Solution:

(a) The location of point "A" with respect to a point on the pavement directly under the luminaire is dimensioned in transverse and longitudinal multiples of the mounting height. Assume that the luminaire distribution provides isolux lines as shown in Fig. B5. Point "A" is then located on this diagram for its position with respect to each luminaire.

(b) Determine the contribution of luminaire 1 and 3 to point "A."

Locate point "A"—Transverse 2 meters to "houseside."

$$\frac{2 \text{ meters}}{10 \text{ meters}} = 0.2 \text{ times mounting height}$$

Longitudinal 33 meters along pavement

$$\frac{33 \text{ meters}}{10 \text{ meters}} = 3.3 \text{ times mounting height}$$

At point "A" for these luminaires, the estimated value from Fig. B5 is 0.08 lux. This is from each luminaire, 1 and 3. Both luminaires together provide 0.16 lux (per 1000 lamp lumens).

(c) Determine contribution of luminaire 2:

Locate point "A"—Transverse 15 meters to "street side."

$$\frac{15 \text{ meters}}{10 \text{ meters}} = 1.5 \text{ times mounting height}$$

(d) Longitudinal locations is 0, directly across from the luminaire. At point "A" for this luminaire, the estimated value from Fig. B5 is 0.17 lux.

The total at point "A" from the three luminaires is 0.16 + 0.17 = 0.33 lux. Because a 20,000-lumen lamp is used, this value must be multiplied by 20, to equal 6.6 lux. However, the subject luminaire mounting height is 10 meters, whereas the test lamp Fig. B5 was at 9 meters. It is therefore necessary to correct the value by multiplying by 0.81 as given for a 10-meter mounting (see table below Fig. B5)—0.81 × 6.6 = 5.3 lux.

The value of 5.3 lux is based on clean luminaires with a lamp producing rated output. To express the level in terms of lux when the illuminating source is at its lowest output and when the luminaire is in its dirtiest condition, it is also necessary to multiply by the LDD factor (0.7) and by the LLD factor (0.85). These factors combine as 0.6. The fully corrected point "A" illuminance value is 5.3 × 0.6 = 3.2 lux. This is the value to compare with the calculated, maintained (depreciated) average lux of 12 for the subject route example.

B3.7 Uniformity ratios. (1) The illuminance uniformity requirements of Table 2(b) of the Standard Practice should be determined by computing the ratio:

$$\frac{\text{Average Horizontal Lux}}{\text{Minimum Horizontal Lux}}$$

Thus, for the prior example, the uniformity at point "A" is:

$$\frac{12 \text{ lux}}{3.2 \text{ lux}} = 3.8{:}1$$

(2) A sufficient number of specific points over the roadway should be checked to ascertain accurately the location and value of the minimum point.

Again, using the subject example and checking point "B":

(a) *Luminaire 1* (Fig. B4):
   "B" is 0.2 MH (Mounting Height) house side and 1½ the spacing or 4.9 MH longitudinal. From Fig. B5, the uncorrected illuminance value is 0.01 lux.

(b) *Luminaire 2:*
   "B" is 1.5 MH street side and ½ the spacing or 1.6 longitudinal. From Fig. B5, the uncorrected value is 0.09 lux.

(c) *Luminaire 3:*
   "B" is 0.2 MH house side and ½ the spacing or 1.6 longitudinal. The Fig. B5 value is 0.5 lux.

The total illuminance from all three luminaires is 0.01 + 0.09 + 0.50 = 0.60 lux, times 20 (lumens in 1000's) = 12 lux. Correcting for a 10-meter instead of 9-meter mounting height gives 0.81 × 12 = 9.7 lux.

The final correction for lamp and dirt depreciation (using the combined factor of 0.6) is 0.6 × 9.7 = 5.8 lux.

The uniformity at point "B" is:

$$\frac{12 \text{ lux}}{5.8 \text{ lux}} = 2.1{:}1$$

This is better than point "A," so "A" is the worst (minimum) point. Because this uniformity (3.8:1) exceeds the recommended value of 3:1 in Table 2(b) this luminaire should *not* be utilized for the subject design problem unless a greater mounting height can be used. For the 10-meter MH, a Type III distribution is probably preferable on this width of road (see Appendix E, Fig. E4).

(3) Some manufacturers are now supplying curves of the type shown in Fig. B6, which indicate the average-to-minimum lux ratio for a particular arrangement of luminaires, as street width and spacing are varied. Such curves are a convenient aid to determine the average-to-minimum illuminance ratios for a given spacing and street width, or to determine the permissible spacing for a required uniformity ratio. They can also be used to determine the relationship between average illuminance and spacing and street width. Each different combination of luminaires, lamp type and arrangement of luminaires will produce a different set of these characteristic curves.

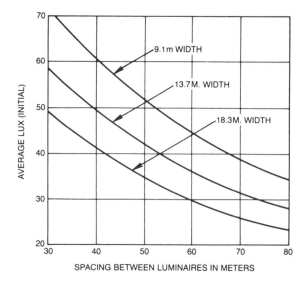

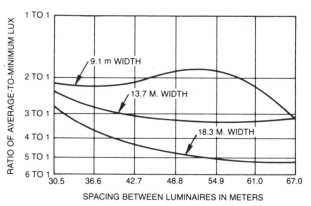

Figure B6. Example of chart showing average lux (left) and average-to-minimum uniformity ratios (right) versus luminaire spacing for staggered arrangement. The values of average lux (initial) are based on an initial lamp output of 30,000 lumens; and the ratio of average lux to minimum lux is the lowest value on the street area. Distribution classification is medium semicutoff, Type II.
Caution: **Values shown on isolux diagrams, etc. may represent actual luminaire light output as shown in the figure; however, they are often shown as a value per 1000 emitted lamp lumens.**

B4. Luminance calculations

Illuminance and luminance values at a point may be calculated from the photometric data obtained and provided by most manufacturers for luminaires associated with roadways. As indicated, parameters of position are important determinations that should be consistently applied for both illuminance and luminance calculation and measurements.

B4.1 Calculation and measurement parameters. (See Figs. B1 and B7.)

Observer eye height: 1.45 meters above grade.

Line of sight of observer: downward one degree below horizontal; parallel to edge of roadway along lines ¼ roadway line width from edges of each lane (2 lines per lane).

Lighting system to be measured: smooth and level at least 10 mounting heights long.

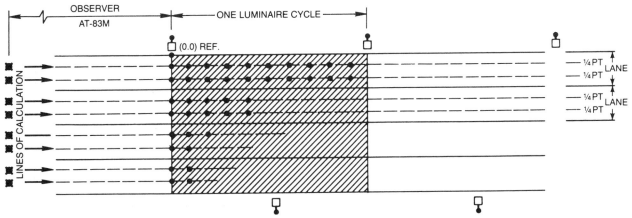

Figure B7. Luminance calculation points. (a) Observer moves with points parallel to roadway (eye height = 1.45 meters; line of sight = 1 degree down over a distance of 83 meters). (b) Area and points are typical as shown: number of points equal to luminaire cycle divided by 10, not to exceed 5 meters between points (minimum of 10 points). (c) Calculations to include a minimum of three luminaire cycles downstream, and one upstream from reference (o.o).

Number of points per line: at least 10, not more than 5 meters apart.

Area covered by measurement and calculations: all points between two luminaires on one side of roadway (Fig. B7).

Calculation point location to contributing luminaires: at least one luminaire behind, and at least three ahead of calculation point (P).

Luminaire light distribution data: based on initial installed values using actual lamp-luminaire performance.

Luminance values: to be calculated using the r-tables B1, B2, B3, and B4: These values will include the value of the indicated "q."

Horizontal illuminance (E_h): to be printed and/or recorded at the same points as luminance values as a reference.

Table B1. r-Table for standard surface R1.[*][†]

β tan γ	0	2	5	10	15	20	25	30	35	40	45	60	75	90	105	120	135	150	165	180
0	655	655	655	655	655	655	655	655	655	655	655	655	655	655	655	655	655	655	655	655
0.25	619	619	619	619	610	610	610	610	610	610	610	610	610	601	601	601	601	601	601	601
0.5	539	539	539	539	539	539	521	521	521	521	521	503	503	503	503	503	503	503	503	503
0.75	431	431	431	431	431	431	431	431	431	431	395	386	371	371	371	371	371	386	395	395
1	341	341	341	341	323	323	305	296	287	287	278	269	269	269	269	269	269	278	278	278
1.25	269	269	269	260	251	242	224	207	198	189	189	180	180	180	180	180	189	198	207	224
1.5	224	224	224	215	198	180	171	162	153	148	144	144	139	139	139	144	148	153	162	180
1.75	189	189	189	171	153	139	130	121	117	112	108	103	99	99	103	108	112	121	130	139
2	162	162	157	135	117	108	99	94	90	85	85	83	84	84	86	90	94	99	103	111
2.5	121	121	117	95	79	66	60	57	54	52	51	50	51	52	54	58	61	65	69	75
3	94	94	86	66	49	41	38	36	34	33	32	31	31	33	35	38	40	43	47	51
3.5	81	80	66	46	33	28	25	23	22	22	21	21	22	22	24	27	29	31	34	38
4	71	69	55	32	23	20	18	16	15	14	14	14	15	17	19	20	22	23	25	27
4.5	63	59	43	24	17	14	13	12	12	11	11	11	12	13	14	14	16	17	19	21
5	57	52	36	19	14	12	10	9.0	9.0	8.8	8.7	8.7	9.0	10	11	13	14	15	16	16
5.5	51	47	31	15	11	9.0	8.1	7.8	7.7	7.7										
6	47	42	25	12	8.5	7.2	6.5	6.3	6.2											
6.5	43	38	22	10	6.7	5.8	5.2	5.0												
7	40	34	18	8.1	5.6	4.8	4.4	4.2												
7.5	37	31	15	6.9	4.7	4.0	3.8													
8	35	28	14	5.7	4.0	3.6	3.2					Q0 = 0.10; S1 = 0.25; S2 = 1.53								
8.5	33	25	12	4.8	3.6	3.1	2.9													
9	31	23	10	4.1	3.2	2.8														
9.5	30	22	9.0	3.7	2.8	2.5														
10	29	20	8.2	3.2	2.4	2.2														
10.5	28	18	7.3	3.0	2.2	1.9														
11	27	16	6.6	2.7	1.9	1.7														
11.5	26	15	6.1	2.4	1.7															
12	25	14	5.6	2.2	1.6															

[*]All values have been multiplied by 10,000. For angles, see Fig. B1.
[†]Adapted from reference 37.

Table B2. r-Table for standard surface R2.*†

β tanγ	0	2	5	10	15	20	25	30	35	40	45	60	75	90	105	120	135	150	165	180
0	390	390	390	390	390	390	390	390	390	390	390	390	390	390	390	390	390	390	390	390
0.25	411	411	411	411	411	411	411	411	411	411	379	368	357	357	346	346	346	335	335	335
0.5	411	411	411	411	403	403	384	379	370	346	325	303	281	281	271	271	271	260	260	260
0.75	379	379	379	368	357	346	325	303	281	260	238	216	206	206	206	206	206	206	206	206
1	335	335	335	325	292	291	260	238	216	195	173	152	152	152	152	152	152	141	141	141
1.25	303	303	292	271	238	206	184	152	130	119	108	100	103	106	108	108	114	114	119	119
1.5	271	271	260	227	179	152	141	119	108	93	80	76	76	80	84	87	89	91	93	95
1.75	249	238	227	195	152	124	106	91	78	67	61	52	54	58	63	67	69	71	73	74
2	227	216	195	152	117	95	80	67	61	52	45	40	41	45	49	52	54	56	57	58
2.5	195	190	146	110	74	58	48	40	35	30	27	24	26	28	30	33	35	38	40	41
3	160	155	115	67	43	33	26	21	18	17	16	16	17	17	18	21	22	24	26	27
3.5	146	131	87	41	25	18	15	13	12	11	11	11	11	11	12	14	15	17	18	21
4	132	113	67	27	15	12	10	9.4	8.7	8.2	7.9	7.6	7.9	8.7	9.6	11	12	13	15	17
4.5	118	95	50	20	12	8.9	7.4	6.6	6.3	6.1	5.7	5.6	5.8	6.3	7.1	8.4	10	12	13	14
5	106	81	38	14	8.2	6.3	5.4	5.0	4.8	4.7	4.5	4.4	4.8	5.2	6.2	7.4	8.5	9.5	10	11
5.5	96	69	29	11	6.3	5.1	4.4	4.1	3.9	3.8										
6	87	58	22	8.0	5.0	3.9	3.5	3.4	3.2											
6.5	78	50	17	6.1	3.8	3.1	2.8	2.7												
7	71	43	14	4.9	3.1	2.5	2.3	2.2												
7.5	67	38	12	4.1	2.6	2.1	1.9													
8	63	33	10	3.4	2.2	1.8	1.7													
8.5	58	28	8.7	2.9	1.9	1.6	1.5													
9	55	25	7.4	2.5	1.7	1.4														
9.5	52	23	6.5	2.2	1.5	1.3														
10	49	21	5.6	1.9	1.4	1.2														
10.5	47	18	5.0	1.7	1.3	1.2														
11	44	16	4.4	1.6	1.2	1.1														
11.5	42	14	4.0	1.5	1.1															
12	41	13	3.6	1.4	1.1															

Q0 = 0.07; S1 = 0.58; S2 = 1.80

*All values have been multiplied by 10,000. For angles, see Fig. B1.
†Adapted from reference 37.

Luminance (L): to be printed and/or recorded at the same points as horizontal illuminance values.

Average luminance (L_{avg}): to be determined by averaging all values of the evaluated roadway section.

Longitudinal luminance uniformity: lane uniformity (L_L) to be determined as the ratio of the maximum-to-minimum luminance in any one single quarter-lane line, taking the worst (highest ratio) as the rating for the roadway.

Average luminance uniformity (L_{avg}): to be determined by rating the average luminance (L_{avg}) to the minimum found in any of the lines within the roadway.

Maximum luminance uniformity (L_{max}): to be determined by rating the maximum luminance found in any of the lines to the minimum found in any of the lines within the roadway.

Table B5 is an illustration of a luminaires's distribution of luminous intensity.

The IES proposes to develop a simplified method of luminance calculations as a separate publication to supplement this Standard Practice.

B5. Calculation procedure for high mast interchange lighting

B5.1 Introduction. The computation of roadway luminance as previously described in this Appendix is not applicable for area lighting with high mast equipment. The reason for this is lack of applicable experience either in this country or overseas in the design of such lighting on a luminance basis or in consideration of pavement reflectance values. Past experience has indicated that a system designed to an illuminance criteria meeting the values in Table 3 of this Standard Practice will give satisfactory results.

High mast interchange lighting is defined as the lighting of a large area by means of a group of luminaires that are designed to be mounted in a fixed orientation (usually level) at the top of a high mast (generally 20 meters or higher). The area will normally contain a group of roadways such as an interchange or parking lots. (This procedure is not applicable for luminaires with both vertical and horizontal adjustments to be made on site, which is termed floodlighting.)

The high mast computation procedure will indicate an approximate number of luminaires per pole and pole spacing to provide the intended average illuminance and uniformity over the area in question. Specific locations for the poles are then determined to insure that all locations on the individual roadways within the area receive illuminance levels at least as high as the minimum value required to meet the uniformity criteria. There are a number of methods for computing high mast interchange lighting sys-

Table B3. r-Table for standard surface R3.*†

θ / tan γ	0	2	5	10	15	20	25	30	35	40	45	60	75	90	105	120	135	150	165	180
0	294	294	294	294	294	294	294	294	294	294	294	294	294	294	294	294	294	294	294	294
0.25	326	326	321	321	317	312	308	308	303	298	294	280	271	262	258	253	249	244	240	240
0.5	344	344	339	339	326	317	308	298	289	276	262	235	217	204	199	199	199	199	194	194
0.75	357	353	353	339	321	303	285	267	244	222	204	176	158	149	149	149	145	136	136	140
1	362	362	352	326	276	249	226	204	181	158	140	118	104	100	100	100	100	100	100	100
1.25	357	357	348	298	244	208	176	154	136	118	104	83	73	70	71	74	77	77	77	78
1.5	353	348	326	267	217	176	145	117	100	86	78	72	60	57	58	60	60	60	61	62
1.75	339	335	303	231	172	127	104	89	79	70	62	51	45	44	45	46	45	45	46	47
2	326	321	280	190	136	100	82	71	62	54	48	39	34	34	34	35	36	36	37	38
2.5	289	280	222	127	86	65	54	44	38	34	25	23	22	23	24	24	24	24	24	25
3	253	235	163	85	53	38	31	25	23	20	18	15	15	14	15	15	16	16	17	17
3.5	217	194	122	60	35	25	22	19	16	15	13	9.9	9.0	9.0	9.9	11	11	12	12	13
4	190	163	90	43	26	20	16	14	12	9.9	9.0	7.4	7.0	7.1	7.5	8.3	8.7	9.0	9.0	9.9
4.5	163	136	73	31	20	15	12	9.9	9.0	8.3	7.7	5.4	4.8	4.9	5.4	6.1	7.0	7.7	8.3	8.5
5	145	109	60	24	16	12	9.0	8.2	7.7	6.8	6.1	4.3	3.2	3.3	3.7	4.3	5.2	6.5	6.9	7.1
5.5	127	94	47	18	14	9.9	7.7	6.9	6.1	5.7										
6	113	77	36	15	11	9.0	8.0	6.5	5.1											
6.5	104	68	30	11	8.3	6.4	5.1	4.3												
7	95	60	24	8.5	6.4	5.1	4.3	3.4												
7.5	87	53	21	7.1	5.3	4.4	3.6													
8	83	47	17	6.1	4.4	3.6	3.1													
8.5	78	42	15	5.2	3.7	3.1	2.6													
9	73	38	12	4.3	3.2	2.4														
9.5	69	34	9.9	3.8	3.5	2.2														
10	65	32	9.0	3.3	2.4	2.0														
10.5	62	29	8.0	3.0	2.1	1.9														
11	59	26	7.1	2.6	1.9	1.8														
11.5	56	24	6.3	2.4	1.8															
12	53	22	5.6	2.1	1.8															

Q0 = 0.07; S1 = 1.11; S2 = 2.38

*All values have been multiplied by 10,000. For angles, see Fig. B1.
†Adapted from reference 37.

tems. Two basic procedures are described as follows:

(1) *Method A* utilizes curves similar to those illustrated in Figures B8 and B9 as aids in calculating initial trial values of luminaire quantities and pole spacing. These curves may be computed by the luminaire manufacturer.

(2) *Method B* does not require the availability of these curves but utilizes an assumed spacing ratio as a starting point for determining the initial trial values.

After the trial values have been determined by either method, the exact placement of poles and luminaires are determined.

The general procedure for determining maintained illuminance includes the steps described in Section B3. It is important that these be followed and the various factors determined before proceeding with the special computations.

B5.2 Initial considerations. Determine the outline of the area to be lighted and select a tentative pole height. This height may be limited by soil conditions, maintenance concerns, grade differences, or other special factors. Select a tentative luminaire and lamp type.

B5.2.1 Method A.

(*1*) Calculate the area ratio (AR) by the for-

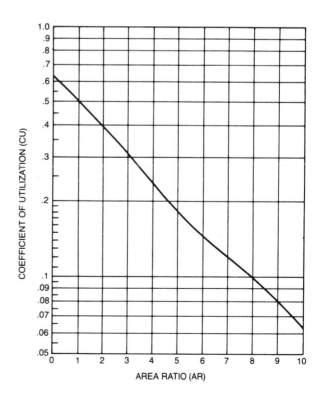

Figure B8. Example of CU (Coefficient of Utilization) versus AR (Area Ratio) curve.

Table B4. r-Table for standard surface R4.[*][†]

β tan γ	0	2	5	10	15	20	25	30	35	40	45	60	75	90	105	120	135	150	165	180
0	264	264	264	264	264	264	264	264	264	264	264	264	264	264	264	264	264	264	264	264
0.25	297	317	317	317	317	310	304	290	284	277	271	244	231	224	224	218	218	211	211	211
0.5	330	343	343	343	330	310	297	284	277	264	251	218	198	185	178	172	172	165	165	165
0.75	376	383	370	350	330	304	277	251	231	211	198	165	139	132	132	125	125	125	119	119
1	396	396	396	330	290	251	218	198	185	165	145	112	86	86	86	86	86	87	87	87
1.25	403	409	370	310	251	211	178	152	132	115	103	77	66	65	65	63	65	66	67	68
1.5	409	396	356	284	218	172	139	115	100	88	79	61	50	50	50	50	52	55	55	55
1.75	409	396	343	251	178	139	108	88	75	66	59	44	37	37	37	38	40	41	42	45
2	409	383	317	224	145	106	86	71	59	53	45	33	29	29	29	30	32	33	34	37
2.5	396	356	264	152	100	73	55	45	37	32	28	21	20	20	20	21	22	24	25	26
3	370	304	211	95	63	44	30	25	21	17	16	13	12	12	13	13	15	16	17	19
3.5	343	271	165	63	40	26	19	15	13	12	11	9.8	9.1	8.8	8.8	9.4	11	12	13	15
4	317	238	132	45	24	16	13	11	9.6	9.0	8.4	7.5	7.4	7.4	7.5	7.9	8.6	9.4	11	12
4.5	297	211	106	33	17	11	9.2	7.9	7.3	6.6	6.3	6.1	6.1	6.2	6.5	6.7	7.1	7.7	8.7	9.6
5	277	185	79	24	13	8.3	7.0	6.3	5.7	5.1	5.0	5.0	5.1	5.4	5.5	5.8	6.1	6.3	6.9	7.7
5.5	257	161	59	19	9.9	7.1	5.7	5.0	4.6	4.2										
6	244	140	46	13	7.7	5.7	4.8	4.1	3.8											
6.5	231	122	37	11	5.9	4.6	3.7	3.2												
7	218	106	32	9.0	5.0	3.8	3.2	2.6												
7.5	205	94	26	7.5	4.4	3.3	2.8													
8	193	82	22	6.3	3.7	2.9	2.4													
8.5	184	74	19	5.3	3.2	2.5	2.1													
9	174	66	16	4.6	2.8	2.1														
9.5	169	59	13	4.1	2.5	2.0														
10	164	53	12	3.7	2.2	1.7														
10.5	158	49	11	3.3	2.1	1.7														
11	153	45	9.5	3.0	2.0	1.7														
11.5	149	41	8.4	2.6	1.7															
12	145	37	7.7	2.5	1.7															

Q0 = 0.08; S1 = 1.55; S2 = 3.03

[*]All values have been multiplied by 10,000. For angles, see Fig. B1.
[†]Adapted from reference 37.

mula:

$$AR = \frac{2.5 \times \text{Pole Height} \times \text{Perimeter of Area}}{\text{Area}}$$

(2) Obtain the coefficient of utilization (CU) value from the CU versus AR curve for the luminaire involved (for typical curve, see Fig. B8).

The value for NLP should be rounded off to a whole number.

B5.2.2 Method B

(1) Assume a spacing-to-mounting height ratio typical for the type of luminaire involved. A value of 5 is common.

B5.3 Number of Poles. The number of poles (NP) is dependent on the area and spacing ratio and can be determined by the formula:

$$NP = \frac{\text{Area}}{(H \times SR)}$$

(3) Determine the spacing-to-mounting-height ratio (SR) as a function of the uniformity ratio (UR) desired by use of the SR versus UR curve for the luminaire involved (for a typical curve, see Fig. B9 and Section B5.7).

(4) Calculate the number of luminaires per pole (NLP) using the formula:

$$NLP = \frac{(AMI) \times (MH \times SR)^2}{(LL/L) \times (CU) \times (LLF)}$$

Note: MH = mounting height; LL/L = Lamp Lumens per Luminaire; and LLF = Light Loss Factor.

(2) Assume a value of average distance (pole to outer edge of lighted area) to mounting height ratio. Use this to obtain a coefficient of utilization value from utilization curve for the luminaire involved. (For typical curve see Fig. B10.)

(3) Calculate the total number of luminaires required (NL) using the formula:

$$NL = \frac{(AMI) \times (A)}{(LL/L) \times (CU) \times (LLF)}$$

A = Area

B5.4 Pole locations. From an isolux chart of the type shown in Fig. B10, determine two boundaries (usually circles); one for the minimum initial illuminance and the other for one-half the minimum initial illuminance value as follows:

(1) Minimum initial illuminance is average

Table B5—Example of Luminaire Distribution of Luminous Intensity

ACTUAL CANDLEPOWER VALUES FOR 22000. LUMENS. TEST NO 100715.

DEG H	0.0	6.5	14.9	24.9	34.8	44.8	54.9	64.9	69.9	74.9	79.9	84.9
0.0	4631.	4631.	4631.	4631.	4631.	4631.	4631.	4631.	4631.	4631.	4631.	4631.
2.5	4580.	4648.	4580.	4648.	4535.	4580.	4558.	4637.	4580.	4626.	4694.	4637.
5.0	4694.	4739.	4694.	4660.	4739.	4535.	4614.	4637.	4614.	4614.	4694.	4660.
7.5	4626.	4626.	4592.	4694.	4694.	4535.	4637.	4637.	4580.	4671.	4524.	4694.
10.0	4626.	4535.	4671.	4637.	4694.	4535.	4592.	4614.	4614.	4603.	4637.	4535.
12.5	4626.	4535.	4614.	4637.	4694.	4580.	4580.	4614.	4671.	4637.	4671.	4614.
15.0	5714.	4648.	5567.	5034.	5601.	4535.	4716.	4694.	4671.	4637.	4660.	4637.
17.5	5759.	4648.	5748.	5555.	5669.	5601.	5669.	4716.	5487.	5068.	4614.	4558.
20.0	5827.	5782.	6145.	5737.	5782.	5714.	5782.	5748.	5657.	5113.	5147.	4592.
22.5	5759.	5669.	5827.	6632.	6961.	5873.	6201.	5850.	5771.	5612.	5147.	4614.
25.0	5782.	5782.	5805.	6825.	6916.	6734.	6224.	5759.	6145.	5850.	5714.	4660.
27.5	5827.	5669.	5748.	6825.	6916.	6916.	6372.	6201.	6258.	5714.	5850.	4716.
30.0	5782.	5782.	5805.	6802.	6734.	6916.	6315.	6258.	6315.	5805.	5816.	4671.
32.5	5782.	5669.	5771.	6712.	5782.	6576.	6394.	6360.	6179.	5771.	5805.	5113.
35.0	5782.	5827.	5714.	6621.	5782.	5759.	6394.	6315.	5725.	5771.	5771.	5090.
37.5	5646.	5669.	5691.	6247.	5827.	5873.	6236.	6734.	5725.	5805.	5793.	4660.
40.0	4694.	5442.	5487.	5669.	5759.	5669.	5771.	6167.	5771.	5827.	5669.	4558.
42.5	4535.	4739.	4637.	5691.	5487.	5714.	5578.	5748.	5748.	5725.	5204.	4614.
45.0	4422.	4535.	4149.	4614.	3492.	4648.	4535.	5771.	5748.	5714.	5147.	4694.
47.5	3560.	4308.	3038.	3877.	3560.	4308.	4467.	5748.	5657.	5204.	5034.	4580.
50.0	3447.	3515.	2880.	2744.	2267.	3560.	4388.	5680.	5090.	5034.	4694.	4614.
52.5	2267.	3288.	2347.	2211.	2313.	3401.	3560.	4671.	4637.	4614.	4614.	4524.
55.0	2381.	2267.	1757.	2211.	2381.	2313.	3310.	4535.	4592.	4535.	4637.	4592.
57.5	1338.	2267.	1723.	2256.	2381.	2267.	2880.	4569.	4592.	4614.	5782.	4614.
60.0	1134.	1179.	1236.	2324.	2426.	2381.	3503.	4637.	5714.	5748.	6904.	5816.
62.5	1224.	1338.	1213.	2335.	2358.	2381.	3447.	4671.	6791.	7313.	8582.	6848.
65.0	907.	1179.	1122.	1723.	2199.	2381.	3560.	6201.	6201.	7981.	11383.	9093.
67.5	907.	1247.	1088.	1213.	1224.	2472.	3174.	5873.	5601.	9013.	13627.	12516.
70.0	907.	1111.	1066.	1179.	1134.	2267.	2041.	3458.	5056.	9682.	13627.	15872.
72.5	0.	159.	57.	703.	1066.	1224.	1236.	2369.	4558.	9217.	12437.	15759.
75.0	45.	0.	23.	159.	113.	1179.	1077.	1723.	3905.	8662.	8038.	10850.
77.5	159.	0.	102.	23.	113.	907.	136.	1667.	2369.	4580.	3889.	5147.
80.0	91.	113.	68.	136.	113.	0.	68.	612.	556.	1780.	1213.	2211.
82.5	45.	45.	45.	91.	45.	159.	79.	102.	125.	1100.	136.	1088.
85.0	45.	45.	0.	45.	45.	113.	136.	79.	23.	159.	45.	136.
87.5	0.	45.	0.	45.	0.	45.	91.	181.	136.	181.	159.	23.
90.0	0.	0.	204.	0.	0.	45.	0.	91.	45.	136.	113.	102.
92.5	204.	204.	159.	181.	159.	0.	102.	68.	45.	136.	91.	113.
95.0	159.	159.	159.	159.	159.	204.	181.	0.	0.	45.	45.	102.
97.5	159.	159.	159.	159.	159.	159.	159.	102.	0.	0.	23.	68.
100.0	159.	159.	159.	136.	113.	159.	136.	204.	204.	0.	0.	45.
102.5	159.	159.	113.	113.	113.	159.	113.	159.	159.	204.	204.	0.
105.0	113.	159.	113.	113.	113.	113.	113.	136.	113.	181.	159.	102.
107.5	113.	113.	113.	113.	113.	113.	113.	136.	113.	181.	159.	159.
110.0	113.	113.	113.	113.	91.	91.	91.	113.	113.	113.	113.	159.
112.5	113.	113.	113.	91.	91.	91.	91.	113.	113.	113.	113.	136.
115.0	113.	113.	91.	91.	45.	45.	45.	91.	91.	113.	113.	136.
117.5	91.	91.	91.	91.	45.	45.	45.	45.	91.	91.	91.	125.
120.0	91.	91.	45.	45.	45.	45.	45.	45.	68.	45.	45.	91.
122.5	0.	0.	0.	0.	0.	0.	0.	0.	0.	0.	0.	0.
180.0	0.	0.	0.	0.	0.	0.	0.	0.	0.	0.	0.	0.

DEG H	89.9	94.9	104.9	114.9	124.9	134.9	144.9	154.9	164.9	174.9	179.9
0.0	4631.	4631.	4631.	4631.	4631.	4631.	4631.	4631.	4631.	4631.	4631.
2.5	4648.	4637.	4614.	4614.	4671.	4637.	4660.	4660.	5034.	4637.	4648.
5.0	4614.	4614.	4637.	4648.	4648.	4716.	5045.	4716.	4637.	4671.	4648.
7.5	4546.	4580.	4127.	4592.	4637.	4648.	4592.	5056.	4694.	4614.	4535.
10.0	4569.	4444.	4501.	4104.	4070.	4682.	4059.	5011.	4592.	4614.	4694.
12.5	4614.	4501.	4490.	3968.	3934.	3979.	3503.	4660.	4501.	4580.	3560.
15.0	4580.	4535.	4070.	3781.	3503.	3481.	3481.	3424.	3503.	3481.	3560.
17.5	4614.	4546.	3945.	3747.	3526.	3583.	3333.	3413.	3549.	3447.	3515.
20.0	4592.	4580.	3481.	3520.	3424.	3447.	2800.	2834.	2347.	3197.	2381.
22.5	4660.	4535.	3549.	3515.	3254.	2823.	2347.	2392.	2313.	2290.	2358.
25.0	4671.	4467.	3481.	3447.	2823.	2347.	2256.	2313.	2222.	2347.	2086.
27.5	4558.	4501.	3401.	3333.	2392.	2290.	2267.	2199.	1190.	1712.	1247.
30.0	4671.	4501.	3481.	2744.	2369.	2313.	1610.	1667.	1213.	1179.	1134.
32.5	4637.	4467.	3537.	2365.	2426.	2143.	1213.	1213.	1270.	1315.	1292.
35.0	4660.	4648.	3424.	2744.	2256.	2041.	1156.	1236.	1270.	1292.	1338.
37.5	4569.	4467.	3481.	2857.	2313.	1644.	1338.	1315.	1292.	1134.	1134.
40.0	4422.	3991.	3481.	3413.	2267.	1689.	1315.	1315.	1134.	1179.	1224.
42.5	4490.	3991.	3526.	3469.	2778.	2177.	1190.	1315.	1202.	1247.	1292.
45.0	4422.	3591.	3481.	3503.	3356.	2426.	1315.	1338.	1270.	1338.	2086.
47.5	4524.	4501.	3424.	3526.	3481.	2330.	1236.	1179.	2109.	2120.	2313.
50.0	4558.	4694.	3424.	3345.	3197.	2301.	1179.	1224.	2154.	2256.	2313.
52.5	4535.	4614.	3537.	2993.	2857.	2058.	1202.	1247.	2199.	2290.	2381.
55.0	4444.	4524.	3456.	2970.	2721.	2075.	1156.	1292.	2177.	2324.	2381.
57.5	4648.	4546.	3549.	2857.	2449.	2109.	1236.	1247.	2063.	2347.	2267.
60.0	5725.	4614.	3560.	2880.	2449.	2177.	1179.	1270.	1292.	2165.	1224.
62.5	7279.	5158.	3481.	2846.	2324.	1644.	1213.	1179.	1213.	1281.	1224.
65.0	10226.	7936.	3447.	2347.	1655.	1236.	533.	1179.	590.	1247.	1111.
67.5	15385.	10872.	3526.	1825.	1270.	1202.	45.	204.	159.	1066.	159.
70.0	14818.	13140.	3345.	1043.	79.	1009.	79.	23.	23.	136.	91.
72.5	10906.	10328.	2392.	45.	136.	57.	23.	136.	159.	23.	159.
75.0	6757.	7426.	1100.	102.	45.	79.	79.	45.	23.	113.	45.
77.5	3537.	4422.	136.	0.	181.	23.	136.	147.	0.	0.	204.
80.0	1179.	1757.	113.	159.	113.	181.	102.	136.	159.	204.	159.
82.5	113.	907.	57.	113.	68.	113.	68.	113.	79.	181.	113.
85.0	136.	57.	136.	91.	45.	45.	23.	102.	23.	102.	45.
87.5	102.	23.	113.	45.	45.	23.	0.	79.	23.	45.	0.
90.0	159.	159.	113.	45.	23.	0.	57.	0.	0.	0.	0.
92.5	113.	113.	91.	45.	0.	0.	204.	57.	204.	102.	204.
95.0	113.	113.	45.	23.	0.	0.	181.	204.	181.	204.	159.
97.5	45.	68.	23.	0.	0.	204.	159.	159.	159.	159.	159.
100.0	45.	45.	0.	102.	204.	159.	159.	159.	113.	159.	113.
102.5	102.	0.	204.	181.	159.	159.	113.	113.	102.	113.	113.
105.0	204.	204.	159.	159.	159.	136.	113.	113.	68.	45.	45.
107.5	159.	181.	159.	159.	113.	113.	102.	102.	45.	45.	45.
110.0	136.	159.	159.	113.	113.	113.	45.	68.	45.	23.	0.
112.5	113.	159.	113.	113.	91.	91.	45.	45.	0.	45.	0.
115.0	113.	113.	113.	113.	91.	45.	45.	45.	0.	23.	0.
117.5	91.	113.	91.	91.	45.	45.	0.	0.	0.	0.	0.
120.0	91.	91.	45.	68.	45.	23.	0.	0.	0.	0.	0.
122.5	0.	0.	0.	0.	0.	0.	0.	0.	0.	0.	0.
180.0	0.	0.	0.	0.	0.	0.	0.	0.	0.	0.	0.

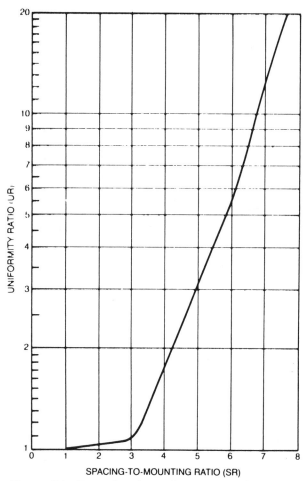

Figure B9. Example of spacing-to-mounting height ratio to average-to-minimum uniformity ratio curve.

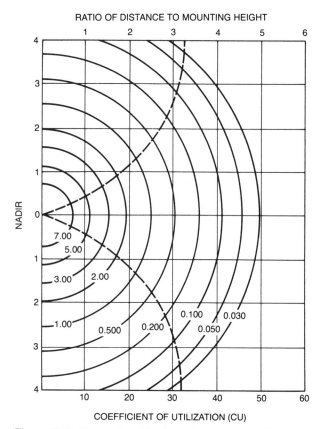

Figure B10. Example of isolux diagram and utilization curves on pavement (mounting height; 30 meters) for symmetric luminaire (110,000 lumen lamp). Dashed curve shows lumen utilization (in percent).

maintained illuminance divided by (Uniformity Ratio × Light Loss Factor).

(2) Either draw circles to scale or prepare templates to scale and superimpose these on the layout making certain that all roadway areas are covered by the minimum illuminance boundaries or by the overlap of two one-half minimum illuminance level boundaries.

(3) If the luminaires on a pole are not symmetric and are at varied orientations, the isolux chart should be a composite representing the array on the pole. Otherwise use the chart for an individual luminaire and multiply the curve values by the number of luminaires per pole.

B5.5 Recalculations. If suitable mounting locations can be found, determine by inspection if higher or lower pole heights may be more suitable, or if one or more poles should be located differently. Repeat the calculations above for a new trial and continue to repeat until a satisfactory solution is reached.

B5.6 Coefficient of utilization vs. area ratio curve. The curve shown in Fig. B8 can be prepared by combining concepts from the zonal cavity method with elements from the flux transfer theory.* Calculations are made in which:

(1) Area corresponds to cavity;

(2) Area Ratio corresponds to cavity ratio;

(3) Area-plane corresponds to work-plane.

The fraction of luminaire flux reaching the area-plane (which represents CU) is then determined for an arbitrary series of area ratios. This is done on a computer by summing the downward flux in a nested series of conic solid angles, ranging from nadir to horizontal about the luminaire. The flux, adjusted by zonal multipliers, are added together and then multiplied by the total downward utilization of the luminaire to produce the various CU values. (The CU for an area ratio of zero is taken equal to the total downward utilization of the luminaire.) The overall results can then be displayed in a CU versus AR curve. Such a curve can be prepared for either a symmetric or an asymmetric luminaire.

B5.7 Spacing ratio vs. uniformity ratio curve. This curve can be determined by calculating the uniformity ratio within a square shaped area bounded by four of the luminaires in question. All the luminaires are to face in the same direction. Each side of the square equals the spacing distance. This involves point calculations and can best be accomplished by use of a computer. Uniformity is to be calculated for a sufficient number of spacing-to-

---

* Material on these two subjects appears in the *IES Lighting Handbook, 1981 Reference Volume*, starting on page 9-6 under "Cavity Ratios" and on page 9–37 under "Coefficient Tables."

mounting height ratios to develop a curve such as that shown in Fig. B9. This is primarily applicable to symmetric luminaires but can be used with asymmetric luminaires with little loss in accuracy.

B6. Computation of walkway and bikeway illuminance

B6.1 Introduction. The procedure to determine the horizontal illuminance values on pedestrian ways for safe and comfortable use is similar to that followed for roadways as explained in the various steps under Section B3. In the case of isolated pedestrian ways, such as park walkways and Type B bikeways where the lighting provided is exclusively for the walkway and is arranged on either one or both sides of the paved area, the procedure is identical to computing roadway illuminance values, even to the point of using street side data from various luminaire curves. In the case of sidewalks (adjacent to roadways) and Type A bikeways, the procedure is very nearly the same as for roadway computation except that the house side curve data is often used. Because the area to be lighted for a Type A bikeway (roadside) is virtually identical to a sidewalk area, the sidewalk computation procedure suggested herein can be assumed to apply also for Type A bikeways (without further mention below to bikeways).

Because the design of roadway lighting places greater emphasis on achieving proper illuminance on the roadway, it is customary that the lighting system be initially selected to suit the needs of the roadway. Then, the system is checked to determine if the sidewalk illuminance levels and uniformity are adequate. If desired sidewalk requirements are lacking, the designer may modify the luminaire type and/or spacing or may provide supplemental lighting primarily for the sidewalk area, or may implement a combination of both techniques to achieve proper illuminance on both roadway and sidewalk. This procedure is sometimes reversed when greater emphasis is placed on the need for adequate sidewalk lighting, in which case Type I or II luminaires or post top luminaires are initially chosen primarily for sidewalk distribution and, when found satisfactory, are later checked for adequacy of roadway illuminance level and uniformity.

In some areas where personal security is a problem and identification of another pedestrian at a distance is important, the recommended levels on the right-hand side of Table 4 in the Standard Practice apply. These recommendations are stated in terms of the average vertical illuminance reaching a plane surface 1.8 meters above the walkway and perpendicular to the centerline of the walkway. The calculation procedure for vertical illuminance is discussed in paragraph B6.3.

B6.2 Determining horizontal illuminance. To calculate the average level of illuminance on the entire sidewalk with luminaires in their maintained condition, proceed as follows:

(1) Determine the coefficient of utilization (CU) for the sidewalk area only, as in paragraph B3.5.2., being sure to subtract from these calculations that portion of the CU that is related to flux falling on the street itself due to the transverse location of the luminaire.

(2) Calculate the average maintained illuminance level on the sidewalk due solely to the immediately adjacent luminaires, using the formula given in paragraph B3.5.3.

(3) For the same sidewalk area, determine the CU for the street side of the luminaires across the street.

(4) Calculate the average maintained illuminance level on the sidewalk due solely to the luminaires across the street, and add to that the illuminance coming from the luminaires on the same side of the street.

(5) Having calculated the average illuminance level across the entire sidewalk, it is now necessary to calculate the minimum level of illuminance, as described in paragraph B3.6 in order to compute the uniformity ratio.

B6.3 Determining vertical illuminance for security areas. The vertial illuminance at a specific point can be calculated by the inverse-square method of calculating illuminance (See the current edition of the *IES Lighting Handbook, Reference Volume*).[1] In this method, the candlepower of the luminaire at the particular angle involved is normally obtained from a luminous intensity chart, as shown in Table B5. The relevant geometry is shown in Fig. B11. The general form of the relationship is given by:

$$E_v = \frac{I(\phi, \gamma) \times \sin\gamma \times \sin\phi \times LLF}{D^2}$$

If it is assumed that the typical pedestrian facial area is approximately 1.8 meters above the sidewalk,

Figure B11. Geometric relationship for determining vertical illuminance on the face of a pedestrian.

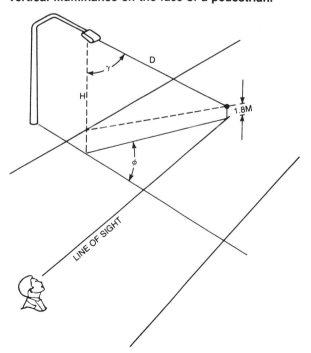

then:

$$D^2 = \frac{(MH - 1.8)^2}{\cos^2\gamma}$$

Therefore:

$$E_v = \frac{I(\phi, \gamma) \times \sin\gamma \times \cos^2\gamma \times \sin\phi \times LLF}{(MH - 1.8)^2}$$

where

$I(\phi, \gamma)$ = source intensity from a luminous intensity distribution chart for a specific luminaire.

A sufficient number of points over the sidewalk should be checked to ascertain accurately that the location and value of the minimum point has been obtained. Only those luminaires that illuminate the vertical plane facing the viewer ($0 \leq \phi \leq 180$ degrees) should be included. If illuminance is of a nonsymmetrical nature, then both directions of pedestrian travel should be analyzed.

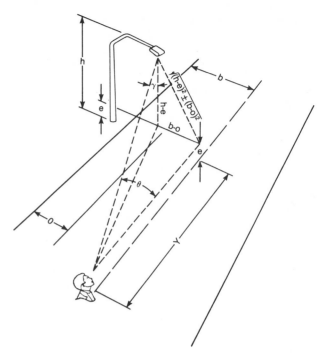

Figure C1. Angular relationships for calculating L_v (Veiling Luminance) from a single luminaire.
Note:

$$\gamma = \text{arc tan} \frac{\sqrt{y^2 + (b \text{ - } o)^2}}{h \text{ - } e}$$

$$\theta = \text{arc tan} \frac{\sqrt{(h \text{ - } e)^2 + (b \text{ - } o)^2}}{y}$$

where
h = mounting height of luminaire above the road surface in meters
e = eye height above the road surface in meters

Appendix C—Glare

(This Appendix is not part of the "American National Standard Practice for Roadway Lighting," ANSI/IES RP-8, 1983, but is included for information purposes only.)

C1 Introduction

The common term "glare," as it affects human vision, is subdivided into two components, disability glare and discomfort glare. They are not completely indivisible but can be approached on a separate basis. Disability glare (veiling luminance) is considered in Section C2, and discomfort glare is discussed in Section C3.

C2 Veiling luminance (L_v)

For most roadway lighting conditions, stray light produced within the eye by discontinuity of brightnesses (usually light sources) with the field of view must be taken into consideration. Stray light within the eye produces a veiling luminance (L_v) which is superimposed upon the retinal image of the object to be seen. This alters the apparent brightness of any object within the visual field and the background against which it is viewed, thereby impairing the ability of the driver to perform visual tasks.

While veiling luminance cannot be completely eliminated, the recommendations of Table 2(a) of the Standard Practice indicate that the sum of the L_v from all the luminaires in the lighting system when viewed from the observer's position should not exceed a specified percent of the average roadway luminance (L_{avg}).

C2.1 Calculation of veiling luminance. The L_v (expressed in candelas per square meter) of a roadway lighting system can be calculated from the ob-

server's position by using the following empirically derived formula[194] calculating the L_v contributed for each luminaire separately, and then summing the individual L values:

$$L_v = \frac{10\,E_v}{\theta^2 + 1.5\theta}$$

where
E_v = vertical illuminance in the plane of the pupil of the observer's eye in lux.
θ = the angle between the line of sight and the luminaire in degrees.
Note: The line of sight is a line parallel to the curb line of the roadway located from the edge of the roadway in one of the quarter-lane planes and at an eye height of 1.45 meters above the road. (See Fig. C1.)

Number of luminaire cycles to be the same as those for determining pavement luminance. The L_v for an entire system of "n" luminaires is therefore:

$$L_v \sum_{i=1}^{n} \frac{10\,E_{vi}}{\theta^2 + 1.5\theta}$$

C2.2 Field measurements. The L_v can be measured

at a particular location with a photoelectric tele-photometer equipped with a special lens system.

C3. Discomfort glare

Discomfort glare does not reduce the ability to see an object as in the case of disability glare, but it produces a sensation of ocular discomfort. It should be noted that discomfort glare may cause fatigue which may result in driver error.

Discomfort glare as well as disability glare are related to the light flux produced, source size, displacement angle of the source, illuminance at the eye, adaptation level, surrounding luminance, exposure time, and motion. The degree in which these factors affect each form of glare varies. Only the illuminance at the eye and the angle of flux entrance into the eye are common to both.

It is generally true that when disability glare is reduced, there will also be a reduction in discomfort glare, but not necessarily in the same relative amount. On the contrary, it is entirely possible to reduce the discomfort glare of a system but at the same time increase the disability glare.

There are currently studies underway to ascertain the relative comfort-discomfort of roadway lighting systems, but results at present are preliminary and inconclusive. The CIE* method of evaluating discomfort glare (the "Glaremark System") is also being studied to determine whether it can be used appropriately in evaluating discomfort glare on roadway lighting systems used in North America.

No system has been adopted by the IES for calculation of relative visual comfort for roadways; however, as soon as data are available, the IES will prepare a suitable evaluation system.

---

* Commission Internationale de l'Éclairage.

Appendix D— Visibility

(This Appendix is not part of the "American National Standard Practice for Roadway Lighting," ANSI/IES RP-8, 1983, but it is included for information purposes only.)

D1. Introduction

The human eye cannot see the light that strikes the pavement. It can only react to the pattern of light that is reflected in its direction. Several factors have been shown to influence visibility within the roadway environment. Many laboratory studies have shown that visual performance is mainly dependent upon the following visual factors:

(1) Luminance adaptation level to which the eye is exposed

(2) Size and shape of the object to be seen

(3) Time available for seeing

(4) Contrast between the object and the background

(5) Contrast between portions of the object

Of the variables mentioned above, contrast is the one most conveniently used by the lighting designers to enhance visibility. Contrast is simply whether an object is sufficiently different in brightness (either brighter or darker) to be distinguished from the background it is seen against.

Contrast is defined as equal to:

$$\frac{(L_t) - (L_b)}{(L_b)} = \frac{\Delta L}{L_b}$$

where L_t = object luminance and
L_b = background luminance

and where object and background luminances are measured in terms of physical photometric units. If contrast is close to zero, the object will probably not be seen, even if the color of the object differs considerably from the background.

The luminance of an object in the roadway is, like the roadway itself, a function of the amount of light falling on it and its own reflectance. In order to develop a system of specification, calculation, and measurement, it is desirable to standardize the dimensions and reflectance of such an object (see Section D3.1.1). This approach permits the luminance distribution to be the only variable when determining the visibility of the object.

A scale of visibility has been developed through experiments with the driving public. A brief discussion of that history is contained in Section D2. The remainder of this Appendix is devoted to a discussion of the concepts used in design of lighting systems based on how much visibility they provide.

D2. Theoretical and empirical basis

A unified conceptual framework has been developed over the last quarter-century for dealing with visibility requirements in an operating situation. Blackwell[164–168] has demonstrated, based on psychophysical research, that visual performance potential for a specific visual task may be determined by comparison with a reference task performed under standardized lighting conditions. This research attempts to describe the effective visual threshold (i.e., borderline between seeing and not seeing an object) for all visual tasks under all viewing situations. Visual performance potential is dependent upon the specification of task contrast and knowledge of contrast sensitivity as a function of the adaptation of the driver. The inclusion of a factor to account for the negative effects of disability glare is also likewise established. (For a comprehensive statement, see Reference 45.)

The quantification of visibility developed by

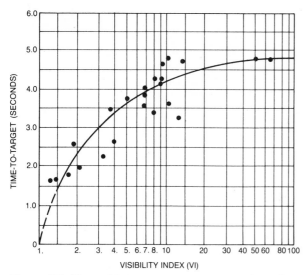

Figure D1. Mean driver response to target detection.

Blackwell has allowed the development of a relationship between the visibility provided to a driver and his performance under that visibility condition. Gallagher[177] developed a method for monitoring vehicle velocity and location as an unsuspecting motorist reacted to a traffic problem. A gray "traffic cone" was placed in the middle lane of a six-lane urban street with light traffic. The driver avoided the cone by braking or changing lanes. The responses of over 1300 drivers under 23 visibility conditions were unobtrusively observed. The basic performance measure was the time to collision from the moment the unalerted driver reacted to the target, assuming no change in vehicle velocity.

The results shown in Fig. D1 indicate that approximately 90 percent of the maximum level of performance that can be influenced by changes in the illumination are obtained with a visibility index (VI) of 15. It would not be cost effective to provide higher levels of visibility for this situation. This result applies only to the particular detection task studies by Gallagher. Other studies are required before general conclusions concerning optimum visibility design levels can be reached.

The development of a system of visibility quantification and the suggestion of a driver performance criterion have little merit if they cannot be related to the ultimate roadway safety criterion—accident reduction. Janoff[56] has reported on a study of the relationship between urban automobile accidents and several measures of lighting effectiveness at 84 locations in the Philadelphia area. These measures included: average horizontal illuminance, average pavement luminance and several variations of visibility measure, including the visibility index, as defined by Gallagher.[67,177,178]

The regression analysis indicated that fewer nighttime, dry weather accidents occur as visibility is increased. However, it was found that this correlation between the visibility index and accidents was significant only after the accident data had been further reduced by the addition of factors for the area

type (*i.e.*, central business district or not) and population density.

D3. Concepts needed for design

The Visibility Index (VI) of a particular target is given by the following expression:

$$VI = \frac{\Delta L}{L_b} \times RCS \times DGF \times TAF$$

Each of these factors is discussed in detail in the sections which follow.

In general, the first factor, $\Delta L/L_b$, is the measured physical task contrast between the luminance pattern of the target and its immediate surroundings. The RCS (Relative Contrast Sensitivity) represents the relative sensitivity of the typical driver in perceiving contrast under conditions approximating those of the roadway under consideration (same adaptation level) compared with the same driver's sensitivity at perceiving a standardized laboratory task under specified illumination conditions. The DGF (Disability Glare Factor accounts for the reduction in visual performance due to veiling luminance (see Appendix C) of light sources near the target.

An additional factor is sometimes used to account for transient adaptation (TAF), the effect of moving the fixation of the eye to other parts of the visual field and the manner in which luminance values in these other areas differ from those near the target. For most night highway applications, TAF can be assumed to be near unity and can be deleted from the calculation. However, when there are large discontinuities in the driver's luminous environment, such as at the entrance of a dark tunnel in daytime, TAF will become an important consideration.

D3.1 Contrast. As discussed in Section D1, the primary component of any visibility measurement system is the determination of contrast for a reference or standard target. The characteristics of one version of a proposed standard target are discussed in Section D3.1.1. Sections D3.1.2 and D3.1.3 discuss the physical quantities that must be determined to calculate contrast.

Visual perception, at least at the threshold level for simple stimuli, is the direct result of perceived differences in background (L_b) and target (L_t) luminances. This difference would be termed perceived contrast if subjective scales for brightness sensitivity were available. Since perceived brightness is difficult to measure—particularly in the field—an approximation of this sensation is provided by a pure ratio of physically measured stimuli level. This ratio is termed Contrast (C) and is defined as:

$$C = \frac{L_t - L_b}{L_b} = \frac{\Delta L}{L_b}$$

This form of the ratio is the most general, in that it can be conveniently used for objects either darker or brighter than the background, since ΔL represents the numerical difference of the two luminances. The ratio of contrast as described above is bounded by -1 and $+\infty$. Negative contrast cases (sometimes called

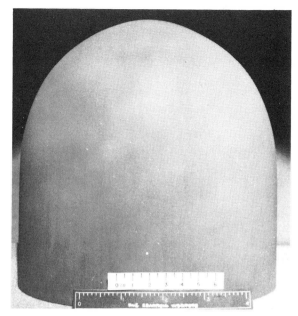

Figure D2. Target used in the Janoff study. [54-56]

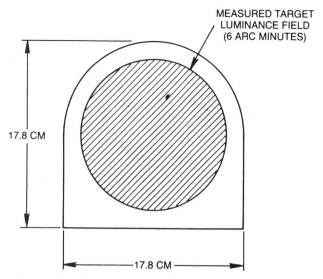

Figure D3. Target configuration showing position of measured target luminance field.

silhouette) occur when the target luminance is less than that of the roadway. A null contrast occurs when the luminance of the target and background are equal or nearly so. A positive contrast, with the target brighter than the background, may occur (curbing, upper parts of pedestrians) and is sometimes called "reverse silhouette."

The contrast ratio is an approximation of the visibility value of a specific background luminance condition. Since objective sensitivity to contrast is related to the level of the background luminance, contrast in its pure form is useful only as a relative comparison of target visibilities under a single background luminance level.

D3.1.1 Reference target. A long history of debate exists on what constitutes a suitable target for the assessment and prescription of roadway lighting quality. The simplest and most commonly used targets have been two-dimensional, of uniform color, and typically low reflectance.

Such targets are easy to use and the calculations concerning their luminance are much more straightforward; however, two-dimension targets fail to reveal the spatial quality to the light. In the roadway design problem, the lighting designer is dealing with discrete light source locations, and the spatial quality of the light can be of major importance. A review of the relevant visibility research literature indicates that a suitable visibility assessment target should be relatively small, close to the roadway, lacking any internal contrast or shadow, and should present a three-dimensional surface toward the driver.

Such a target is shown in Figs. D2 and D3. This target is a hemisphere of 18 centimeters nominal diameter mounted on a cylinder of the same diameter and height. This size is the smallest object capable of eliciting an evasion response from motorists, *i.e.*, a typical vehicle will not pass over this target without impact. In addition, its three-dimensional shape permits the reflection of light from all sources which

is analogous to real objects typical of the roadway environment. While the choice of target reflectance is arbitrary, the one shown in Fig. D2 has a diffuse 18 percent gray reflectance that approximates the observed 15th percentile finish of pedestrian clothing.

D3.1.2 Target luminance. Target luminance (L_t) may be visualized as the light reflected from reference targets placed at intervals along the roadway. Because target luminance will be different depending on target location within a lighted roadway, contrast and VI will vary as well; therefore, it should be determined for targets on the centerline of each lane employing at least 10 points located halfway between each two parallel grid points used for determining pavement luminance (see Appendix B4). Target luminance is a function of the vertical illuminance from each luminaire in the layout directed toward the target, times the directional reflectance of the target toward the oncoming driver. In the case of the target discussed above, the reflectance is 0.18. If the geometry is as illustrated in Fig. D4, then:

$$L_t = 0.18 \frac{I \sin\gamma \, \sin\phi \, \cos^2\gamma}{DZ^2}$$

L_t can also be measured photometrically using an aperture as shown in Fig. D3.

Figure D4. Definitions of geometry between luminaire and grid target point on roadway.

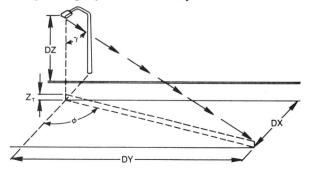

D3.1.3 Background luminance. Background luminance (L_b) employed in the determination of contrast is the luminance of the area immediately surrounding the reference visibility target. When placed on the roadway, as described in Section D3.1.2, the average of the pavement luminance (see Appendix B2) on each side of the target should be utilized to calculate the contrast at each point separately. The value of L_b can also be measured with a luminance meter (or telephotometer) using a conventional circular or "split-slit" type aperture.

D3.2 Relative contrast sensitivity. The contrast of an object against its background determines whether it can be seen and is, therefore, the basic element of visibility. However, only a limited scale of contrast can be developed using this concept because the ability of the human eye to discern contrast is dependent on the luminance level to which that eye is adapted. The CIE has developed a scale of relative contrast sensitivity (RCS) factors to take this difference into account.[45] This scale was developed by assigning unity contrast sensitivity for the standard observer at a task background luminance equal to 100 candelas per square meter. The RCS for any observer can be calculated using the following formula:

$$RCS = n \left[\left(\frac{S}{tL} \right)^{0.4} + 1 \right]^{-2.5}$$

and

$$n = \left[\left(\frac{s}{100t} \right)^{0.4} + 1 \right]^{2.5}$$

where L is the task background luminance (candelas per square meter) and t and S are parameters defined as follows: t is related to the age (A) of the observer.

For Age 20–30 years   Log t = 0
     30–44 years   = −0.01053 (A − 30)
     44–64 years   = −0.1474−0.0134 (A − 44)
     64–80 years   = −0.4154−0.0175 (A − 64)

S is related to the size of the task detail, its location relative to the line of sight and the age (A) of the observer.

Log S = 0.5900 − 0.6235 log d − 0.1980X − s

where
d = size of task in minutes
X = degrees task is off the line of sight axis
s = 0   for age 20–44
s = 0.00406 (A − 44)   44–64
s = 0.0812 + 0.00667 (A − 64)   64–80

The average pavement luminance is assumed to approximate the adaptation luminance of the driver. The RCS term is used to factor the pure contrast values obtained in section D3.1 so that a common scale is produced across a wide range of adaptation levels.

The importance of using the RCS factor can be seen in the following example. If the physical contrast is equal to 1.0 and the adaptation luminance is 0.2 candelas per square meter, then the effective contrast can be determined as follows:

$$C_{eff} = C \times RCS$$

An RCS value of 0.08 is calculated from the formula above for a 22-year old observer looking at a 4-minute target with a luminance of 0.2 candelas per square meter when the target is on the axis of the line-of-sight. Then:

$$C_{eff} = 1.0 \times 0.08 = 0.08$$

However, if the adaptation level is raised to 1.0 candelas per square meter, then the RCS equals 0.211, and the same effective contrast can be achieved with a physical contrast of only 0.38. This result is obtained by using the equation and solving for C when C_{eff} is equal to 0.08 and RCS is equal to 0.21. This illustrates why one sees equal contrast tasks better when there is more luminance. If a criterion level of effective contrast is determined in order to accomplish a certain level of visual performance, it is possible to trade off physical contrast (C) and adaptation luminance (L_b) through the RCS factor.

D3.3 Disability glare factor. The Disability Glare Factor (DGF) is used to reduce the effective contrast C_{eff} for the effect of veiling luminance (L_v) present in the visual field. The origin, measurement and calculation of veiling luminance is discussed in Appendix C. The DGF is composed of two terms. The first serves to reduce the C_{eff} by the estimate of visibility loss that L_v represents and the second serves to increase C_{eff} by the gain arising out of increased adaptation due to the presence of L_v. The first effect is always larger than the second.

The DGF is calculated by first determining the change in adaptation luminance (L_b) due to the presence of L_v:

$L_{b'}$ = Background luminance plus veiling luminance divided by a correction for sphere base glare in laboratory data:

$$L_{b'} = \frac{L_b + L_v}{1.074}$$

DGF is then determined from the following equation:

$$DGF = \frac{L_b}{L_{b'}} \times \frac{RCS'}{RCS}$$

where:
RCS = Relative Contrast Sensitivity for a luminance equal to L_b as calculated from the above formula.
RCS′ = Relative Contrast Sensitivity for a luminance equal to $L_{b'}$ as calculated from the formula above.
The DGF is always less than one.

D4. Setting performance standards

Based on the relationships discussed in Section D2, it is possible to view the VI as a scale of visibility quantified in a way compatible with object detection needs of drivers. However, it is not immediately obvious how much visibility is required to satisfy the safety and operational needs of drivers in a given geometric and traffic situation.

Designing roadway lighting requires knowledge of the visibility needs of drivers in terms of the more subtle information flow which characterizes the great majority of driving activity and time. Knowledge in this area is far from complete. The most sophisticated models of human information flow continue to fall short of describing the dynamic real world visual experience. Partly for this reason, it should be recognized that the specification of lighting in the near future will be based on empirical models of visibility. The prescription of the quantity of illumination will perhaps remain bound to a rather arbitrary scale of hazard or visual demand as implied in the roadway classification system currently employed.

As with the development of any new science, the application of its principles occurs almost simultaneously with the development of the principles themselves. This process can lead to some awkward moments as researchers and designers attempt to stretch their knowledge and needs to the limit. For this reason, the discussion of visibility has been provided as an Appendix to this Standard Practice with the hope of encouraging users to experiment with its utility. Out of such experimentation, hopefully, an understanding of the value and the establishment of design requirements will be made.

Appendix E—Classification of luminaire light distributions

(This Appendix is not part of the "American National Standard Practice for Roadway Lighting," ANSI/IES RP-8, 1983, but is included for information purposes only.)

E1. Introduction

(1) Proper distribution of the light flux from luminaires is one of the essential factors in efficient roadway lighting. The light emanating from the luminaires is directionally controlled and proportioned in accordance with the requirements for seeing and visibility. Light distributions are generally designed for a typical range of conditions that include: luminaire mounting height; transverse (overhang) location of luminaires; longitudinal spacing of luminaires; widths of roadway to be effectively lighted; arrangement of luminaires; percentage of lamp light directed toward the pavement and adjacent areas; and maintained efficiency of the system.

(2) Several methods have been devised for showing the light distribution pattern from a luminaire. (See Figs. E1 through E5.) For practical operating reasons the range in luminaire mounting heights may be kept constant. Therefore, it becomes necessary to have several different light distributions

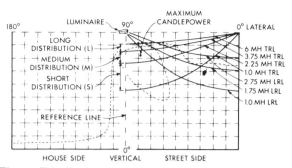

Figure E1. Recommended vertical light distribution boundaries on a rectangular coordinate Grid (representation of a sphere). Dashed lines are isocandela traces.

in order to effectively light different roadway widths, using various luminaire spacing distances at a particular luminaire mounting height. All luminaires can be classifed according to their lateral and vertical distribution patterns. Different lateral distributions are available for different street widths to mounting height ratios; and different vertical distributions are available for different spacing-to-mounting height ratios.

Distributions with higher vertical angles of maximum candlepower emission are necessary to obtain the required illuminance uniformity where longer luminaire spacings are used (as on residential and light traffic roadways). These higher vertical emission angles produce a more favorable pavement brightness which may be desired for silhouette seeing where traffic volume is relatively light. Distributions with lower vertical angles of maximum candlepower emission are used in order to reduce system glare. This becomes more important when using high lumen output lamps. The lower the emission angle, the closer the luminaire spacing must be to obtain required illuminance uniformity. Therefore, to achieve specific illuminance results it becomes necessary as a part of any lighting system design to consider and to check the illuminance uniformity by checking ratios of average illuminance to minimum illuminance.

(3) Luminaire light distribution may be classified

Figure E2. Typical roadway lighting layout showing spacing-to-mounting height relationships.

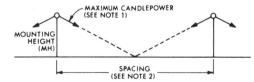

Note 1: Maximum candlepower beams from adjacent luminaires should at least meet on the road surface.

Note 2. Maximum luminaire spacing generally is less than:

    "A"—Short Distribution—4.5 MH;

    "B"—Medium Distribution—7.5 MH; and

    "C"—Long Distribution—12.0 MH

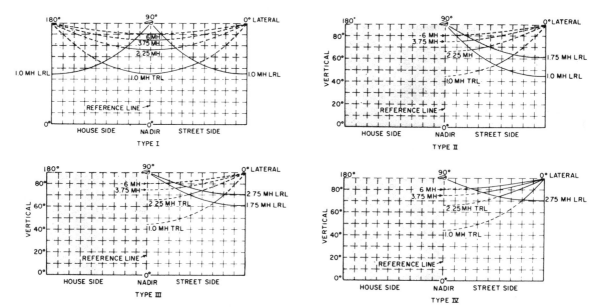

Figure E3. Recommended lateral light distribution boundaries on a rectangular coordinate grid (representation of a sphere).

in respect to three criteria:

    (a) Vertical light distribution

    (b) Lateral light distribution

    (c) Control of light distribution above maximum candlepower

(4) Classification of light distribution should be made on the basis of an isocandela diagram which, on its rectangular coordinate grid, has superimposed a series of Longitudinal Roadway Lines (LRL) in multiples of mounting height (MH), and a series of Transverse Roadway Lines (TRL) in multiples of mounting height. The relationship of LRL and TRL to an actual street, and the representation of such a web, are shown in Figs. E1 through E5. The minimum information that should appear on such an isocandela diagram for classification is as follows:

    (a) LRL lines of 1.0 MH, 1.75 MH, and 2.75 MH

    (b) TRL lines of 1.0 MH, 2.25 MH, 3.75 MH, 6.0 MH, and 8.0 MH

    (c) Maximum candlepower location and half maximum candlepower trace

    (d) Candlepower lines equal to the numerical values of 2½, 5, 10 and 20 percent of the rated bare lamp lumens.

E2. Vertical light distributions

Vertical light distributions are divided into three groups: short (S), medium (M), and long (L). See Figs. E1 and E4.

E2.1 Short distribution. A luminaire is classified as having a short light distribution when its maximum candlepower point lies in the "S" zone of the grid which is from the 1.0–MH TRL to less than the 2.25–MH TRL.

E2.2 Medium distribution. A luminaire is classified as having a medium light distribution when its maximum candlepower point lies in the "M" zone of the grid which is from the 2.25–MH TRL to less than the 3.75–MH TRL.

E2.3 Long distribution. A luminaire is classified as having a long light distribution when its maximum candlepower point lies in the "L" zone of the web which is from the 3.75–MH TRL to less than the 6.0–MH TRL.

E3. Lateral light distributions

Lateral light distributions (see Figs. E3 and E4) are divided into two groups based on the location of the luminaire as related to the area to be lighted. Each group may be subdivided into divisions with regard to the width of the area to be lighted in terms of the MH ratio. Only the segments of the half maximum candlepower isocandela trace that fall within the longitudinal distribution range, as determined by the point of maximum candlepower (short, medium, or long), are used for the purpose of establishing the luminaire distribution width classification.

E3.1 Luminaires at or near center of area. The group of lateral width classifications that deals with luminaires intended to be mounted at or near the center of the area to be lighted has similar light distributions on both the "house side" and the "street side" of the reference line.

    E3.1.1 Type I. A distribution is classified as Type I when its half maximum candlepower isocandela trace lies within the Type I width range on both sides of the reference line which is bounded by 1.0–MH house side. LRL and 1.0–MH street side LRL within the longitudinal distribution range (short, medium, or long) where the point of maximum candlepower falls.

    E3.1.2 Type I, four-way. A distribution is classified as Type I, Four-Way when it has four beams of the width as defined for Type I above.

    E3.1.3 Type V. A distribution is classified as Type

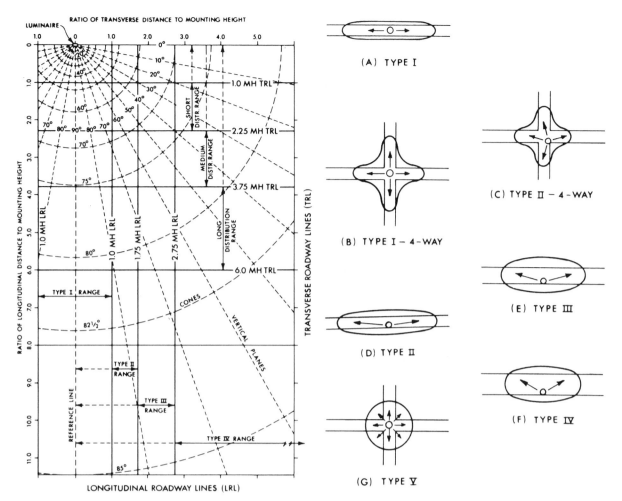

Figure E4. Plan view of roadway coverage for different types of luminaires.

V when the distribution has a circular symmetry of candlepower distribution which is essentially the same at all lateral angles around the luminaire.

E3.2 Luminaires near side of area. The group of lateral width classifications that deals with luminaires intended to be mounted near the side of the area to be lighted vary as to the width of distribution range on the street side of the reference line. The house side segment of the half maximum candlepower isocandela trace within the longitudinal range in which the point of maximum candlepower falls (short, medium, or long) may or may not cross the reference line. In general, it is preferable that the half maximum candlepower isocandela trace remains near the reference line. The variable width on the street side is as defined.

E3.2.1 Type II. A distribution is classified as Type II when the street side segment of the half maximum candlepower isocandela trace within the longitudinal range in which the point of maximum candlepower falls (short, medium, or long) does not cross the 1.75–MH street side LRL.

E3.2.2 Type II, four-way. A distribution is classified as a Type II, Four-Way when it has four beams each of the width on the street side as defined for Type II above.

E3.2.3 Type III. A distribution is classified as Type III when the street side segment of the half maximum candlepower isocandela trace within the longitudinal range in which the point of maximum candlepower falls (short, medium, or long) lies partly or entirely beyond the 1.75–MH street side LRL, but does not cross the 2.75–MH street side LRL.

E3.2.4 Type IV. A distribution is classified as Type IV when the street side segment of the half maximum candlepower isocandela trace within the longitudinal range in which the point of maximum candlepower falls (short, medium, or long) lies partly or entirely beyond the 2.75–MH street side LRL.

E4. Control of distribution above maximum candlepower

Although the pavement brightness generally increases when increasing the vertical angle of light flux emission, it should be emphasized that the disability and discomfort glare also increase. However, since the respective rates of increase and decrease of these factors are not the same, design compromises become necessary in order to achieve balanced performance. Therefore, varying degrees of control of candlepower in the upper portion of the beam above maximum candlepower are required. This control of the candlepower distribution is divided into three categories.

E4.1 Cutoff. A luminaire light distribution is designated as cutoff (C) when the candlepower per 1000

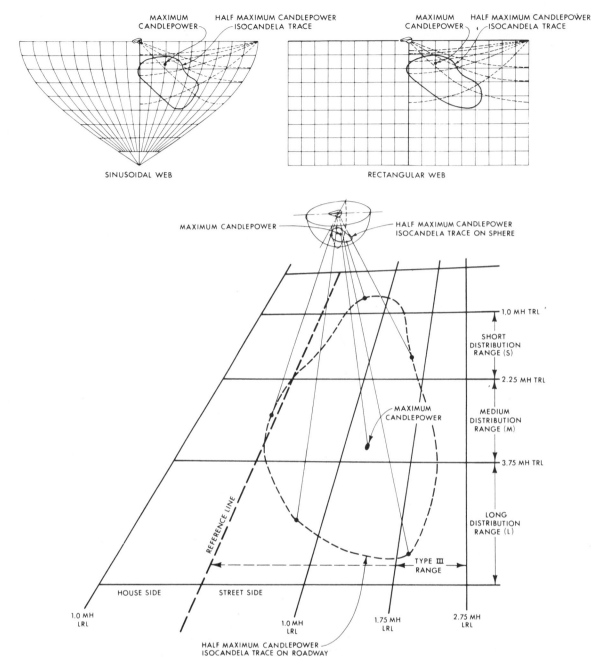

Figure E5. Diagram showing projection of maximum candlepower and half maximum candlepower isocandela trace from a luminaire having a Type III—Medium distribution, on the imaginary sphere and the roadway. Sinusoidal web and rectangular web representation of sphere are also shown, with maximum candlepower and half maximum candlepower isocandela trace.

lamp lumens does not numerically exceed 25 (2½ percent) at an angle of 90 degrees above nadir (horizontal), and 100 (10 percent) at a vertical angle 80 degrees above nadir. This applies to any lateral angle around the luminaire.

E4.2 Semicutoff. A luminaire light distribution is designated as semicutoff (SC) when the candlepower per 1000 lamp lumens does not numerically exceed 50 (5 percent) at an angle of 90 degrees above nadir (horizontal), and 200 (20 percent) at a vertical angle of 80 degrees above nadir. This applies to any lateral angle around the luminaire.

E4.3 Noncutoff. A luninaire light distribution is designated as noncutoff (NC) when there is no candlepower limitation in the zone above maximum candlepower.

E5. Variations and comments

(1) With the variations in roadway width, type of surface, luminaire mounting height, and spacing that may be found in actual practice, there can be a large number of "ideal" lateral distributions. For practical applications, however, a few types of lateral distribution patterns may be preferable to many complex arrangements. This simplification of distribution types will be more easily understood and conse-

quently there will be greater assurance of proper installation and more reliable maintenance.

(2) When luminaires are tilted upward it raises the angle of the street side light distribution. Features such as cutoff or width classification may be changed appreciably. When the tilt is planned, the luminaire should be photometered and the light distribution classified in the position in which it will be installed.

(3) Types I, II, III and IV lateral light distributions should vary across transverse roadway lines other than that including the maximum candlepower in order to provide adequate coverage of the rectangular roadway area involved. The width of the lateral angle of distribution required to cover adequately a typical width of roadway varies with the vertical angle or length of distribution as shown by the TRL (transverse roadway line). For a TRL 4.5–MH, the lateral angle of distribution for roadway coverage is obviously narrower than that required for a TRL 3.0–MH or for a TRL 2.0–MH.

(4) For typical roadway conditions it is desirable to approach very closely the light distributions prescribed. Purposeful variations from these distributions are permissible when such variations become necessary. Several examples of these purposeful variations are:

(*a*) Linear source luminaires which provide broad Type I or Type II distributions and which project the maximum candlepower lower than specified.

(*b*) Directional lighting for one-way streets and divided highways, where the light projected in the direction of traffic is substantially reduced in the high vertical angle.

(*c*) Linear source luminaires parallel to the street to obtain reduced glare and increased utilization.

(*d*) Luminaires mounted at low mounting heights.

(*e*) Types IV and V luminaire distributions with extra upward light for illuminating building fronts.

(*f*) "Offset mounting" style luminaires designed to be located at a lateral distance from the area to be lighted.

Other purposeful variations from the distributions specified may be found advantageous from time to time for special applications.

(5) For high mast installations involving multiple luminaires on one structure or support, the entire group of luminaires may be considered as a single composite luminaire for purposes of determining distribution type, cutoff classification, maximum candlepower, etc. Photometric data may be supplied in this form.

Appendix F—Measurement of performance factors in roadway lighting

(This Appendix is not part of the "American National Standard Practice for Roadway Lighting," ANSI/IES RP-8, 1983, but is included for information purposes only.)

It is both practical and desirable to measure the performance of roadway lighting installations. This may be done at the start-up time of new installations and be compared with previous design predictions. Similar measurements may be made at later dates to determine illuminance depreciation.

Because of the difficulty and expense of making field measurements of pavement luminance (this requires the closure of at least one traffic lane for substantial periods of time), it has been found that those who utilize a computerized design procedure using point calculations can easily generate the horizontal illuminance level at each of the pavement luminance measurement points. As a check on the performance of the lighting system, it is only necessary to measure the illuminance at these points.

Instruments are available and techniques have been established for measuring such factors as:

(1) Illuminance (horizontal and/or vertical lux)

(2) Direct glare

(3) Veiling luminance

(4) Pavement and object luminance

The field measurements of systems require special knowledge and study. For further information on this subject, see the "IES Guide for Photometric Measurement of Roadway Lighting Installations"[25] and the "IES Approved Method for Photometric Testing of Roadway Luminaires."[28]

Appendix G—Metric Conversion Tables

(This Appendix is not part of the "American National Standard Practice for Roadway Lighting," ANSI/IES RP-8, 1983, but is included for information purposes only.)

Table G1. Illuminance Conversion Factors

1 lumen = 1/683 light-watt	1 watt-second = 10^7 ergs
1 lumen-hour = 60 lumen-minutes	1 phot = 1 lumen/square centimeter
1 footcandle = 1 lumen/square foot	1 lux = 1 lumen/square meter = 1 metercandle

Multiply Number of → To Obtain By Number of ↓	Foot-candles	Lux	Phot
Footcandles	1	0.0929	929
Lux	10.76	1	10,000
Phot	0.00108	0.0001	1
Milliphot	1.076	0.1	1,000

Table G2. Conversion Factors for Units of Length

Multiply Number of → To Obtain Number of ↓ By	Angstroms	Nanometers	Micrometers (Microns)	Millimeters	Centimeters	Meters	Kilometers	Mils	Inches	Feet	Miles
Angstroms	1	10	10^4	10^7	10^8	10^{10}	10^{13}	2.540×10^5	2.540×10^8	3.048×10^9	1.609×10^{13}
Nanometers	10^{-1}	1	10^3	10^6	10^7	10^9	10^{12}	2.540×10^4	2.540×10^7	3.048×10^8	1.609×10^{12}
Micrometers (Microns)	10^{-4}	10^{-3}	1	10^3	10^4	10^6	10^9	2.540×10	2.540×10^4	3.048×10^5	1.609×10^9
Millimeters	10^{-7}	10^{-6}	10^{-3}	1	10	10^3	10^6	2.540×10^{-2}	2.540×10	3.048×10^2	1.609×10^6
Centimeters	10^{-8}	10^{-7}	10^{-4}	10^{-1}	1	10^2	10^5	2.540×10^{-3}	2.540	3.048×10	1.609×10^5
Meters	10^{-10}	10^{-9}	10^{-6}	10^{-3}	10^{-2}	1	10^3	2.540×10^{-5}	2.540×10^{-2}	3.048×10^{-1}	1.609×10^3
Kilometers	10^{-13}	10^{-12}	10^{-9}	10^{-6}	10^{-5}	10^{-3}	1	2.540×10^{-8}	3.048×10^{-5}	3.048×10^{-4}	1.609
Mils	3.937×10^{-6}	3.937×10^{-5}	3.937×10^{-2}	3.937×10	3.937×10^2	3.937×10^4	3.937×10^7	1	10^3	1.2×10^4	6.336×10^7
Inches	3.937×10^{-9}	3.937×10^{-8}	3.937×10^{-5}	3.937×10^{-2}	3.937×10^{-1}	3.937×10	3.937×10^4	10^{-3}	1	12	6.336×10^4
Feet	3.281×10^{-10}	3.281×10^{-9}	3.281×10^{-6}	3.281×10^{-3}	3.281×10^{-2}	3.281	3.281×10^3	8.333×10^{-5}	8.333×10^{-2}	1	5.280×10^3
Miles	6.214×10^{-14}	6.214×10^{-13}	6.214×10^{-10}	6.214×10^{-7}	6.214×10^{-6}	6.214×10^{-4}	6.214×10^{-1}	1.578×10^{-8}	1.578×10^{-5}	1.894×10^{-4}	1

Table G3. Luminance Conversion Factors

Multiply Number of → To Obtain Number of ↓ By	Footlambert	Candela/ square meter	Candela/ square inch	Candela/ square foot	Candela/ square centimeter
Footlambert	1	0.2919	452	3.142	2,919
Candela/square meter	3.426	1	1.550	10.76	10.000
Candela/square inch	0.00221	0.000645	1	0.00694	6.45
Candela/square foot	0.3183	0.0929	144	1	929
Candela/square centimeter	0.00034	0.0001	0.155	0.00108	1

Appendix H—Glossary of terms used in roadway lighting

(This Appendix is not part of the "American National Standard Practice for Roadway Lighting," ANSI/IES RP-8, 1983, but it is included for information purposes only.)

absorptance: the ratio of the flux absorbed by a medium to the incident flux.

Note: The sum of the hemispherical reflectance, the hemispherical transmittance, and the absorptance is one.

accommodation: the process by which the eye changes focus from one distance to another.

adaptation: the process by which the visual system becomes accustomed to more or less light or light of a different color than it was exposed to during an immediately preceding period. It results in a change in the sensitivity of the eye to light.

atmospheric transmissivity: the ratio of the directly transmitted flux incident on a surface after passing through unit thickness of the atmosphere to the flux that would be incident on the same surface if the flux had passed through a vacuum.

ballast: a device used with an electric-discharge lamp to obtain the necessary circuit conditions (voltage, current and waveform) for starting and operating.

bikeway: any road, street, path, or way that in

Table H1. Symbols and acronyms.

Acronyms

AASHTO	American Association of State Highway and Transportation Officials
CIE	Commission Internationale de l'Éclairage
IERI	Illuminating Engineering Research Institute
IES	Illuminating Engineering Society of North America
ITE	Institute of Transportation Engineers
JIES	Journal of the Illuminating Engineering Society
LDA	Lighting Design & Application
SAE	Society of Automotive Engineers

English Symbols

A	area
AR	area ratio
CRF	contrast rendition factor
CU	coefficient of utilization
DGF	disability glare factor
E	illuminance
EF	equipment factor
I	intensity (luminous)
L	luminance
LDD	luminaire dirt depreciation factor
LLD	lamp lumen depreciation factor
LLF	light loss factor
LRL	longitudinal roadway line
MF	maintenance factor
MH	mounting height
NL	number of luminaires
NLP	number of luminaires per pole
NP	number of poles
TRL	transverse roadway line
UF	utilization factor
U(R)	uniformity (ratio)
VI	visibility index

Greek Symbols

α	alpha	angle (vertical) at point of observation (See Fig. B1.)
β	beta	angle (horizontal) at point of observation (See Fig. B1.)
γ	gamma	angle (vertical) at luminaire light center (See Fig. B1.)
Δ	delta	change of (a variable)
θ	theta	angle (slant) at point of observer's eye between line of sight and luminaire light center
π	pi	ratio of circumference to diameter
ρ	rho	reflectance (generalized)
φ	phi	angle (horizontal) at point directly under luminaire
Φ	phi	flux (luminous)
ω	omega	solid angle

some manner is specifically designated as being open to bicycle travel, regardless of whether such facilities are designated for the exclusive use of bicycles or are to be shared with other transportation modes. Bikeways are designated as follows:

Type A—designated bicycle lane: a portion of roadway or shoulder that has been designated for use of bicyclists. It is distinguished from the portion of the roadway for motor vehicle traffic by a paint stripe, curb, or other similar device.

Type B—bicycle trail: a separate trail or path from which motor vehicles are prohibited and for the exclusive use of bicyclists or the shared use of bicyclists and pedestrians. Where such trail or path forms a part of a highway, it is separated from the roadways for motor vehicle traffic by an open space or barrier.

blinding glare: glare that is so intense that for an appreciable length of time after it has been removed no object can be seen.

bracket (mast arm): an attachment, to a lamp post or pole, from which a luminaire is suspended.

brightness: see *luminance* and *subjective brightness*.

candela, cd: the SI unit of luminous intensity. One candela is one lumen per steradian. Formerly candle. See Fig. H-1.

candela per square meter: the SI unit of luminance equal to the uniform luminance of a perfectly diffusing surface emitting or reflecting light at the rate of one lumen per square meter or the average luminance of any surface emitting or reflecting light at that rate. The unit is sometimes called a nit.

candlepower, cp: luminous intensity expressed

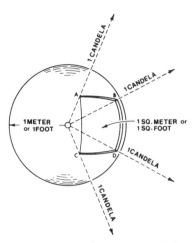

Figure H1. Relationship between candelas, lumens, lux and footcandles.

A uniform point source (luminous intensity or candlepower = one candela) is shown at the center of a sphere of one meter or one foot radius. It is assumed that the sphere surface has zero reflectance.

The illuminance at any point on the sphere is one lux (one lumen per square meter) when the radius is one meter, or one footcandle (one lumen per square foot) when the radius is one foot.

The solid angle subtended by the area, A, B, C, D is one steradian. The flux density is therefore one lumen per steradian, which corresponds to a luminous intensity of one candela, as originally assumed.

The sphere has a total area of 12.57 (4π) square meters or square feet, and there is a luminous flux of one lumen falling on each square meter or square foot. Thus the source provides a total of 12.57 lumens.

in candelas. It is no indication of the total light output.

candlepower distribution curve: a curve, generally polar, representing the variation of luminous intensity of a lamp or luminaire in a plane through the light center.

Note: a vertical candlepower distribution curve is obtained by taking measurements at various angles of elevation in a vertical plane through the light center; unless the plane is specified, the vertical curve is assumed to represent an average such as would be obtained by rotating the lamp or luminaire about its vertical axis. A horizontal candlepower distribution curve represents measurements made at various angles of azimuth in a horizontal plane through the light center.

central (foveal) vision: the seeing of objects in the central or foveal part of the visual field, approximately two degrees in diameter. It permits seeing much finer detail than does peripheral vision.

coefficient of utilization, CU: the ratio of the luminous flux (lumens) from a luminaire received on the surface of the roadway to the lumens emitted by the luminaire's lamp(s) alone.

contrast sensitivity: the ability to detect the presence of luminance differences. Quantitatively, it is equal to the reciprocal of the contrast threshold.

contrast: see *luminance contrast.*

contrast threshold: the minimal perceptible contrast for a given state of adaptation of the eye. It also is defined as the luminance contrast detectable during some specific fraction of the times it is presented to an observer, usually 50 percent.

diffuse reflectance: the ratio of the flux leaving a surface or medium by diffuse reflection to the incident flux.

diffuser: a device to redirect or scatter the light from a source, primarily by the process of diffuse transmission.

direct glare: glare resulting from high luminances or insufficiently shielded light sources in the field of view or from reflecting areas of high luminance. It usually is associated with bright areas, such as luminaires, that are outside the visual task or region being viewed.

directional reflectance coefficient: The reflectance in a particular direction for incident ray leaving a direction of incidence defined by angles β and γ (see Fig. B1). Also, called *bidirectional reflectance-distribution function.*

disability glare: glare resulting in reduced visual performance and visibility. It often is accompanied by discomfort. See *veiling luminance.*

discomfort glare: glare producing discomfort. It does not necessarily interfere with visual performance or visibility.

equivalent luminous intensity (of an extended source at a specified distance): the intensity of a point source which would produce the same illuminance at that distance. Formerly, *apparent luminous intensity of an extended source.*

fluorescent lamp: a low-pressure mercury electric-discharge lamp in which a fluorescing coating (phosphor) transforms some of the ultraviolet energy generated by the discharge into light.

footcandle, fc: the unit of iluminance when the foot is taken as the unit of length. It is the illuminance on a surface one square foot in area on which there is a uniformly distributed flux of one lumen, or the illuminance produced on a surface all points of which are at a distance of one foot from a directionally uniform point source of one candela.

footlambert, fL: a unit of luminance (photometric brightness) equal to $1/\pi$ candela per square foot, or to the uniform luminance of a perfectly diffusing surface emitting or reflecting light at the rate of one lumen per square foot, or to the average luminance of any surface emitting or reflecting light at that rate. Use of this unit is deprecated.

glare: the sensation produced by luminance within the visual field that is sufficiently greater than the luminance to which the eyes are adapted to cause annoyance, discomfort, or loss in visual performance and visibility. See *blinding glare, direct glare, disability glare, discomfort glare.*

Note: the magnitude of the sensation of glare depends upon such factors as the size, position and luminance of a source, the number of sources, and the luminance to which the eyes are adapted.

high intensity discharge (HID) lamp: an electric discharge lamp in which the light producing arc is stabilized by wall temperature, and the arc tube has a bulb wall loading in excess of three watts per square centimeter. HID lamps include groups of lamps known as mercury, metal halide, and high pressure sodium.

high mast lighting: illumination of a large area by means of a group of luminaires which are designed to be mounted in fixed orientation at the top of a high mast (generally 20 meters or higher).

high pressure sodiuum (HPS) lamp: high intensity discharge (HID) lamp in which light is produced by radiation from sodium vapor operating at a partial pressure of about 1.33×10^4 Pa (100 torr). Includes clear and diffuse-coated lamps.

illuminance, $E = d\Phi/dA$: the density of the luminous flux incident on a surface; it is the quotient of the luminous flux by the area of the surface when the latter is uniformly illuminated.

illuminance (lux or footcandle) meter: an instrument for measuring illuminance on a plane. Instruments which accurately respond to more than one spectral distribution are color corrected, *i.e.*, the spectral response is balance to $V(\lambda)$ or $V'(\lambda)$. Instruments which accurately respond to more than one spatial distribution of incident flux are cosine corrected, *i.e.*, the response to a source of unit luminous intensity, illuminating the detector from a fixed distance and from different directions decreases as the cosine of the angle between the incident direction and the normal to the detector surface. The instrument is comprised of some form of photodetector, with or without a filter, driving a digital or analog readout through appropriate circuitry.

illumination: the act of illuminating or state of being illuminated. This term has been used for density of luminous flux on a surface (illuminance) and such use is to be deprecated.

incandescent filament lamp: a lamp in which light is produced by a filament heated to incandescence by an electric current.

infield: the portion of an interchange area exclusive of roadways and shoulders. Such portions may be either landscaped or unimproved.

intensity: a shortening of the terms luminous intensity and radiant intensity. Often misused for level of illumination or illuminance.

isocandela line: a line plotted on any appropriate coordinates to show directions in space, about a source of light, in which the candlepower is the same. For a complete exploration the line always is a closed curve. A series of such curves, usually for equal increments of candlepower, is called an isocandela diagram.

isolux line: one plotted on any appropriate coordinates to show all the points on a surface where the illuminance is the same. For a complete exploration the line is a closed curve. A series of such lines for various illuminance values is called an isolux diagram.

isoluminance line: a line plotted on any appropriate set of coordinates to show all the points on a surface where the luminance is the same. A series of such lines for various luminance values is called an isoluminance diagram.

lambert, L: a unit of luminance equal to $1/\pi$ candela per square centimeter. The use of this unit is deprecated.

lambertain surface: a surface that emits or reflects light in accordance with Lambert's cosine law. A Lambertian surface has the same luminance regardless of viewing angle.

lamp: a generic term for an artificial source of light.

lamp lumen depreciation factor, LLD: the multiplier to be used in illuminance calculations to relate the initial rated output of light sources to the anticipated minimum rated output based on the relamping program to be used.

lamp post: a standard support provided with the necessary internal attachments for wiring and the external attachments for the bracket and luminaire.

lateral width of a light distribution: the lateral angle between the reference line and the width line, measured in the cone of maximum candlepower. This angular width includes the line of maximum candlepower.

light center (of a lamp): the center of the smallest sphere that would completely contain the light-emitting element of the lamp.

light center length (of a lamp): the distance from the light center to a specified reference point on the lamp.

light loss factor, LLF: a factor used in calculating illuminance after a given period of time and under given conditions. It takes into account temperature and voltage variations, dirt accumulation on luminaire and room surfaces, lamp depreciation, maintenance procedures and atmospheric conditions. Formerly called *maintenance factor*.

longitudinal roadway line, LRL: may be any line along the roadway parallel to the curb line.

low pressure sodium lamp: a discharge lamp in which light is produced by radiation from sodium vapor operating at a partial pressure of 0.13 to 1.3 Pa(10^{-3} to 10^{-2} torr).

lumen, lm: SI unit of luminous flux. Radiometrically, it is determined from the radiant power. Photometrically, it is the luminous flux emitted within a unit solid angle (one steradian) by a point source having a uniform luminous intensity of one candela.

luminaire: a complete lighting unit consisting of a lamp or lamps together with the parts designed to distribute the light, to position and protect the lamps and to connect the lamps to the power supply.

luminaire cycle: the distance between two luminaires along one side of the roadway.

Note: this may not be the same as luminaire spacing along the centerline considering *both* sides of the road.

luminaire dirt depreciation (LDD) factor: the multiplier to be used in illuminance calculations to relate the initial illuminance provided by clean, new luminaires to the reduced illuminance that they will provide due to dirt collection on the luminaires at the time at which it is anticipated that cleaning procedures will be instituted.

luminaire efficiency: the ratio of luminous flux

(lumens) emitted by a luminaire to that emitted by the lamp or lamps used therein.

luminance, L = d²Φ/(dω dA cosθ) (in a direction and at a point of real or imaginary surface): the quotient of the luminous flux at an element of the surface surrounding the point, and propagated in directions defined by an elementary cone containing the given direction, by the product of the solid angle of the cone and the area of the orthogonal projection of the element of the surface on a plane perpendicular to the given direction. The luminous flux may be leaving, passing through, and/or arriving at the surface. Formerly, *photometric brightness*.

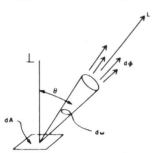

By introducing the concept of luminous intensity, luminance may be expressed as $L = dI/(dA \cos\theta)$. Here, luminance at a point of a surface in a direction is interpreted as the quotient of luminous intensity in the given direction produced by an element of the surface surrounding the point by the area of the orthogonal projection of the element of surface on a plane perpendicular to the given direction. (Luminance may be measured at a receiving surface by using $L = dE/(d\omega \cos\theta)$. This value may be less than the luminance of the emitting surface due to the attenuation of the transmitting media.)

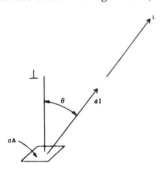

Note: In common usage the term "brightness" usually refers to the strength of sensation which results from viewing surfaces or spaces from which light comes to the eye. This sensation is determined in part by the definitely measurable luminance defined above and in part by conditions of observation such as the state of adaptation of the eye.

In much of the literature the term brightness, used alone, refers to both luminance and sensation. The context usually indicates which meaning is intended. Previous usage notwithstanding, neither the term "brightness" nor the term "photometric brightness" should be used to denote the concept of luminance.

luminance contrast: the relationship between the luminances of an object and its immediate back-

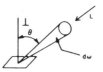

ground. It is equal to $(L_1 - L_2)/L_1$, $(L_2 - L_1)/L_1$ or $\Delta L/L_1$, where L_1 and L_2 are the luminances of the background and object, respectively. The form of the equation must be specified. The ratio $\Delta L/L_1$ is known as Weber's fraction.

Note: See last paragraph of the note under luminance. Because of the relationship among luminance, illuminance and reflectance, contrast often is expressed in terms of reflectance when only reflecting surfaces are involved. Thus, contrast is equal to $(\rho_1 - \rho_2)/\rho_1$ or $(\rho_2 - \rho_1)/\rho_1$ where ρ_1 and ρ_2 are the reflectances of the background and object, respectively. This method of computing contrast holds only for perfectly diffusing surfaces; for other surfaces it is only an approximation unless the angles of incidence and view are taken into consideration.

luminance ratio: the ratio between the luminances of any two areas in the visual field.

Note: see last paragraph of the note under *luminance*.

luminous efficacy of a source of light: the quotient of the total luminous flux emitted by the total lamp power input. It is expressed in lumens per watt.

Note: the term luminous efficiency has in the past been extensively used for this concept.

luminous flux, φ: the time rate of flow of light.

luminous flux density at a surface, dφ/dA: the luminous flux per unit area at a point on a surface.

Note: this need not be a physical surface; it may equally well be a mathematical plane.

luminous intensity, I = dφ/dω: the luminous flux per unit solid angle in a specific direction. Hence, it is the luminous flux on a small surface normal to that direction, divided by the solid angle (in steradians) that the surface subtends at the source.

Note: mathematically, a solid angle must have a point as its apex: the definition of luminous intensity, therefore, applies strictly to a point source. In practice, however, light emanating from a source whose dimensions are negligible in comparison with the distance from which it is observed may be considered as coming from a Point. For extended sources, see *equivalent luminous intensity*.

lux, lx: the SI unit of illuminance. It is the illuminance on a surface one square meter in area on which there is a uniformly distributed flux of one lumen, or the illuminance produced at a surface all points of which are at a distance of one meter from a uniform point source of one candela.

maintenance factor, MF: a factor formerly used to denote the ratio of the illuminance on a given area after a period of time to the initial illuminance of the same area. *See light loss factor.*

mean lamp lumens: the mean lumen output of a lamp is calculated by determining the area beneath the lumen maintenance characteristic curve of that source over a given period of time and dividing that area by the time period in hours.

mercury lamp: a high intensity discharge (HID) lamp in which the major portion of the light is produced by radiation from mercury operating at a partial pressure in excess of 1.013×10^5 Pa (1 atmosphere). Includes clear, phosphor-coated (mercury-fluorescent), and self-ballasted lamps.

metal halide lamp: a high intensity discharge (HID) lamp in which the major portion of the light is produced by radiation of metal halides and their products of dissociation—possibly in combination with metallic vapors such as mercury. Includes clear and phosphor coated lamps.

mounting height, MH: the vertical distance between the roadway surface and the center of the apparent light source of the luminaire.

overhang: the distance between a vertical line passing through the luminaire and the curb or edge of the travelled roadway.

photometric brightness: a term formerly used for *luminance.*

point of fixation: a point or object in the visual field at which the eyes look and upon which they are focused.

primary line of sight: the line connecting the point of observation and the point of fixation.

r-table: a table for a particular pavement type which provides reduced luminance coefficients in terms of the variable β and $\tan\gamma$, as defined by Fig. B1.

rapid start fluorescent lamp: a fluorescent lamp designed for operation with a ballast that provides a low-voltage winding for preheating the electrodes and initiating the arc without a starting switch or the application of high voltage.

reaction time: the interval between the beginning of a stimulus and the beginning of the response of an observer.

reduced luminance coefficient, r: the value at a point on the pavement defined by angles β and γ (see Fig. B1) which, when multiplied by the appropriate luminous intensity from a luminaire and divided by the square of the mounting height, will yield the pavement luminance at that point produced by the luminaire.

reference line: either of two radial lines where the surface of the cone of maximum candlepower is intersected by a vertical plane parallel to the curb line and passing through the light center of the luminaire.

reflectance of a surface or medium: the ratio of the reflected flux to the incident flux.

Note: measured values of reflectance depend upon the angles of incidence and view, and on the spectral character of the incident flux. Because of this dependence, the angles of incidence and view, and the spectral characteristics of the source should be specified.

reflector: a device used to redirect the luminous flux from a source by the process of reflection.

refractor: a device used to redirect the luminous flux from a source, primarily by the process of refraction.

regular (specular) reflectance: the ratio of the flux leaving a surface or medium by regular (specular) reflection to the incident flux.

setback: the lateral offset of the pole from face of curb or edge of travelled way.

shielding angle (of a luminaire): the angle between a horizontal line through the light center and the line of sight at which the bare source first becomes visible.

spacing: the distance between successive luminaires measured along the center line of the street. See Fig. B2 and also see *luminaire cycle.*

spacing-to-mounting height ratio, S/MH: the ratio of the distance between luminaire centers to the mounting height above the roadway.

subjective brightness: the subjective attribute of any light sensation giving rise to the perception of luminous intensity, including the whole scale of qualities of being bright, light, brilliant, dim, or dark.

Note: the term brightness often is used when referring to the measurable "luminance." While the context usually makes it clear as to which meaning is intended, the preferable term for the photometric quantity is luminance, thus reserving brightness for the subjective sensation.

transverse roadway line, TRL: may be any line across the roadway that is perpendicular to the curb line.

tungsten-halogen lamp: a gas filled tungsten incandescent lamp containing a certain proportion of halogens.

Note: the tungsten-iodine lamp (UK) and quartz-iodine lamp (USA) belong to this category.

utilization efficiency: a plot of the quantity of light falling on a horizontal plane both in front of and behind the luminaire. It shows only the percent of bare lamp lumens which fall on the horizontal surface, and is plotted as a ratio of width of area to mounting height of the luminaire.

veiling luminance: a luminance superimposed on the retinal image which reduces its contrast. It is this veiling effect produced by bright sources or areas in the visual field that results in decreased visual performance and visibility.

veiling reflection: regular reflections superimposed upon diffuse reflections from an object that partially or totally obscure the details to be seen by reducing the contrast. This sometimes is called reflected glare.

visibility: the quality or state of being perceivable by the eye. In many outdoor applications, visibility is defined in terms of the distance at which an object can be just perceived by the eye. In indoor applications it usually is defined in terms of the contrast or size of a standard test object, observed under standardized view-conditions, having the same threshold as the given object.

visibility index, VI: a measure closely related to *visibility level* used in connection with road lighting applications.

visibility level, VL: a contrast multiplier to be applied to the visibility reference function or provide the luminance contrast required at different levels of task background luminance to achieve visibility for specified conditions relating to the task and observer.

visual acuity: a measure of the ability to distinguish fine details. Quantitatively, it is the reciprocal of the angular separation in minutes of two lines of width subtending one minute of arc when the lines are just resolvable as separate.

visual angle: the angle subtended by an object or detail at the point of observation. It usually is measured in minutes of arc.

walkway: a sidewalk or pedestrian way.

width line: the radial line (the one that makes the larger angle with the reference line) that passes through the point of one-half maximum candlepower on the lateral candlepower distribution curve plotted on the surface of the cone of maximum candlepower.

zonal constant: a factor by which the mean candlepower emitted by a source of light in a given angular zone is multiplied to obtain the lumens in the zone.

Appendix I—Bibliography

(This Appendix is not part of the "American National Standard Practice for Roadway Lighting," ANSI/IES RP-8, 1983, but is included for information purposes only.)

General reference

1. *IES Lighting Handbook*, *1981 Reference Volume*, New York: Illuminating Engineering Society of North America, 1981.
2. *IES Lighting Handbook*, *1981 Application Volume*, New York: Illuminating Engineering Society of North America, 1981.
3. *IES Lighting Handbook*, 5th Edition, New York: Illuminating Engineering Society of North America, 1972.
4. *Lighting Handbook*, Bloomfield, NJ: Westinghouse Electric Corp., 1973.
5. *Lighting Manual*, Eindhoven: N.V. Philips Gloeilampenfabrieken, 1975.
6. *EEI Street Lighting Manual*, 2nd Edition, New York: Edison Electric Institute, 1969.
7. *Roadway Lighting Handbook*, Washington, D.C.: Federal Highway Administration, 1978.
8. Ketvirtis, A, *Highway Lighting Engineering*, Toronto: Foundation of Canada Engineering Corp., 1967.
9. de Boer, J. B. (Editor), *Public Lighting*, Eindhoven: Philips Technical Library, 1967.
10. van Bommel, W. J. M. and de Boer, J. B., *Road Lighting*, Kluwer Technische Boeken B.V.: Philips Technical Library, 1980 (available from Scholium International, Inc.)

North American practices and guides

11. IES Roadway Lighting Committee, "American National Standard Practice for Roadway Lighting," *J. Illum. Eng. Soc.*, Oct. 1977, p. 16.
12. "American National Standard Practice for Roadway Lighting," *J. Illum. Eng. Soc.*, July 1972, p. 334.
13. IES Roadway Lighting Committee, "American Standard Practice for Roadway Lighting," *Illum. Eng.*, Feb. 1964, p. 73.
14. IES Committee on Street Highway Lighting, "American Standard Practice for Street and Highway Lighting," New York: Illuminating Engineering Society, 1953.
15. IES Committee on Street and Highway Lighting, "American Standard Practice for Street and Highway Lighting," New York: Illuminating Engineering Society, 1947.
16. IES Committee on Street and Highway Lighting, "Recommended Practice of Street and Highway Lighting," *Illum. Eng.*, Feb. 1946, p. 103.
17. IES Committee on Street and Highway Lighting, "Recommended Practice of Street Lighting," *Illum. Eng.*, Jan. 1941, p. 17.
18. IES Committee on Street and Highway Lighting, "Code of Highway Lighting," *Trans. IES*, Feb. 1937, p. 141.
19. IES Street Lighting Committee, "Code of Street Lighting," *Trans. IES.*, Jan. 1935, p. 96.
20. IES Committee on Street Lighting, "Code of Street Lighting," *Trans. IES* Jan. 1931, p. 15.
21. IES Committee on Street Lighting, "Principles of Street Lighting," *Trans. IES*, July 1928, p. 615.
22. "An Informational Guide for Roadway Lighting," Washington, D.C.: American Association of State Highway and Transportation Officials, 1976.
23. IES Roadway Lighting Committee, "Lighting Tunnels," *J. Illum. Eng. Soc.*, April 1972, p. 247.
24. IES Roadway Lighting Committee, "Lighting Roadway Safety Rest Areas," *J. Illum. Eng. Soc.*, Oct. 1974, p. 75.
25. IES Testing Procedures Committee, "IES Guide for Photometric Measurement of Roadway Lighting Installations," *J. Illum. Eng. Soc.*, Jan. 1975, p. 154.
26. IES Roadway Lighting Committee, "Roadway Sign Illumination," *J. Illum. Eng. Soc.*, Oct. 1974, p. 78.
27. IES Testing Procedures Committee, "IES Guide for Photometric Measurements of Roadway Sign Installations," *J. Illum. Eng. Soc.*, July 1976, p. 244.
28. IES Testing Procedures Committee, "IES Approved Method for Photometric Testing of Roadway Luminaires," *J. Illum. Eng. Soc.*, Jan. 1978, p. 132.
29. IES Committee on Store Lighting, "Recommended Practice of Outdoor Parking Area Lighting," *Illuminating Engineering*, May 1960, p. 307.
30. IES Roadway Lighting Committee, "Lighting Traffic Tunnels and Underpasses," *Illuminating Engineering*, June 1957, p. 325.
31. IES Testing Procedures Committee, "IES Approved Method for Determining Luminaire-Lamp-Ballast Combination Operating Factors for High Intensity Discharge Luminaires," *Illuminating Engineering*, Dec. 1970, p. 718.
32. "Application and Presentation of Photometric Data for Street Lighting Luminaires," EEI/NEMA Publication No. 69–31, Washington, D.C.: Edison Electric Institute/National Electrical Manufacturers Association.
33. IES Testing Procedures Committee, "IES Approved Method for Life Testing of High Intensity Discharge Lamps," *J. Illum. Eng. Soc.*, July 1981, p. 211.

CIE practices and guides

34. *Recommendations for the Lighting of Roads for Motorized Traffic*, CIE 12.2, Washington, D.C.: National Bureau of Standards, 1977.
35. *Recommendations for Motorway Lighting*, CIE 23, Washington, D.C.: National Bureau of Standards, 1972.
36. *International Recommendations for Tunnel Lighting*, CIE 26, Washington, D.C.: National Bureau of Standards, 1973.
37. *Calculation and Measurement of Luminance and Illuminance in Road Lighting*, CIE 30, Washington, D.C.: National Bureau of Standards, 1976.
38. *Glare and Uniformity in Road Lighting Installations*, CIE 31, Washington, D.C.: National Bureau of Standards, 1976.
39. *Depreciation and Maintenance of Public Lighting Installations*, CIE 33A/33B, Washington, D.C.: National Bureau of Standards, 1977.
40. *Road Lighting Lantern and Installation Data—Photometrics, Classification and Performance*, CIE 34, Washington, D.C.: National Bureau of Standards, 1977.
41. *Road Lighting and Accidents*, CIE 8.2, second draft, Washington, D.C.: National Bureau of Standards, to be published.
42. *Road Lighting for Wet Conditions*, CIE 47, Washington, D.C.: National Bureau of Standards, 1979.
43. *Photometry of Luminaires for Street Lighting*, CIE 27, Washington, D.C.: National Bureau of Standards, 1973.
44. *A Unified Framework of Methods for Evaluating Visual Performance Aspects of Lighting*, CIE 19, Washington, D.C.: National Bureau of Standards, 1972.
45. *An Analytic Model for Describing the Influence of Lighting Parameters Upon Visual Performance*, CIE 19/2, Washington, D.C.: National Bureau of Standards, 1980.

46. Austin, B. R. "Public Lighting—The Deadly Reckoning," *Public Lighting*, Sept. 1976, p. 67.

47. Box, P. C. "Effect of Lighting Reduction on an Urban Major Route," *Traffic Engineering*, Oct. 1976, p. 26.

48. Box, P. C., "Relationship Between Illumination and Freeway Accidents," IERI Project 85-67, *Illum. Eng.* May/June 1971, p. 365.

49. Electrical Demonstration Branch of the Tennessee Valley Authority, "A Study of the Benefits of Suburban Highway Lighting," Illum. Eng., April 1969, p. 359.

50. Farouki, O. T., "The Effect of Improved Road Lighting on Accidents At Night," *Public Lighting*, Sept. 1977, p. 74.

51. Fisher, A. J., *A Review of Street Lighting In Relation to Road Safety*, Report No. NR/18, Australian Department of Transport, June 1973.

52. Hargroves, R. A. and Scott, P. P., "Measurements of Road Lighting and Accidents—The Results," *Public Lighting*, Dec. 1979, p. 213.

53. Hilton, M. H., *Continuous Freeway Illumination and Accidents on a Section of Route I-95*, Report No. 79-R4, Charlottsville: Virginia Highway and Transportation Research Council, Aug. 1976.

54. Janoff, M. S., *et al.*, "Driver and Pedestrian Behavior—The Effect of Specialized Crosswalk Illumination," *J. Illum. Eng. Soc.*, July 1977, p. 202.

55. Janoff, M. S., *et al*, *Effectiveness of Highway Arterial Lighting*, Report No. FHWA-RD-77-37, Washington, D.C.: Federal Highway Administration, Offices of Research and Development, 1977.

56. Janoff, M. S., *et al*, "The Relationship Between Visibility and Traffic Accidents," *J. Illum. Eng. Soc.*, Jan. 1978, p. 95.

57. Joint Committee of the Institute of Traffic Engineers and the IES, "Public Lighting Needs," *Illum. Eng.*, Sept. 1966, p. 585.

58. Ketvirtis, A., "Road Illumination and Traffic Safety," *Transport Canada*, Ottawa, Ontario, 1977.

59. Marks, V. J., "Effects of Reduced Intersection Lighting on Nighttime Accident Frequency," *Final Report HR-1003A*, Ames, Iowa: Dept. of Trans., Highway Div., Nov. 1977.

60. Marsden, A. M., "Roadway Lighting Visibility and Accident Reduction," *Public Lighting*, Dec. 1976, p. 106.

61. Richards, S. H., *The Effects of Reducing Continuous Roadway Lighting to Conserve Energy: A Case Study*, 15th Annual SAFE Symposium, College Station: Texas Transportation Institute, Dec. 1977.

62. Russell, E. R., and Konz, S., "Night Visibility of Trains at Railroad-Highway Grade Crossings," Manhattan: Kansas State University, Dec. 1979.

63. Scholz, I., "Street Lighting and Motoring Accidents," *ILR*, 1978/4, p. 120.

64. Tien, J. M., "Lighting's Impact On Crime," *LD&A*, Dec. 1979, p. 20.

65. Walker, F. W. and Roberts, S. E., "Evaluation of Lighting On Accident Frequency at Highway Intersections," *Transportation Research Record 562*, Washington, DC: Transportation Research Board, 1976, p. 73.

66. P. C. Box, "Comparison of Accidents and Illumination," *Highway Research Record No. 416*, Washington, D.C.: National Academy of Sciences, 1972, p. 10.

67. P. C. Box, "Freeway Accidents and Illumination," *Highway Research Record No. 416*, National Academy of Sciences, 1972.

Design and calculations

68. Adrian, W., "On the Influence of Light-Intensity-Distribution of Lights on the Luminance, its Uniformity and Glare in Road Illumination," *Lichttechnik*, No. 2, 1968, p. 15A.

69. Alexander, G. A., *et al*, "Lighting the New Four-Lane Highway Tunnel at Thorold, Ontario," *Illum. Eng.*, March 1970, p. 163.

70. Barr, V., "Improving City Streets for Use at Night—the Norfolk Experiment," *LD&A*, April 1976, p. 25.

71. Blamey, C., "Photometric Measurements and Computer Simulation of the Lighting on the Toronto Bypass of Highway 401," Ontario: Research and Development Division, Ministry of Transportation and Communications, Mar. 1977.

72. Christofferson, F. W., "Investigation of Highway Lighting," Final Report HR-154, Ames, Iowa: Dept. of Trans., Highway Division, Nov. 1976.

73. Clark, F., "The Case for Step-by-Step Procedures for Calcu-

lations in Roadway Lighting Design," *Illum. Eng.*, Nov. 1970, p. 637.

74. Cook, L. F., "Computer-Assisted Design of Street Lighting Service Cabling," *Public Lighting*, June 1976, p. 43.

75. Cossyphas, H. and Stark, R., "Evaluation of an Experimental High-Mount Illumination Technique for Expressway Interchanges," *Illum. Eng.*, Feb. 1971, p. 84.

76. de Boer, J. B., "Road Surface Luminance and Glare Limitation in Lighting for Safe and Comfortable Road Traffic," *Highway Research Board Bulletin 295*, National Research Council, 1961, p. 56.

77. Dorrington, J. W., "Conservation," *Public Lighting*, Mar. 1975, p. 6.

78. Elmer, W. B., "Pedestrian Walkway Lighting Comes into its Own," *Illum. Eng.*, June 1967, p. 377.

79. Ewing, J. L., "Extending the Coefficient of Utilization," *J. Illum. Eng. Soc.*, July 1978, p. 207.

80. Ewing, J. L. and Keck, M. E., "Street Lighting Luminaire Distributions for Uniform Luminance and Illumination," *J. Illum. Eng. Soc.*, Apr. 1978, p. 190.

81. Faucett, R. E. and Frier, J. P., "Roadway Lighting Design from Extra High Mounting Heights," *J. Illum. Eng. Soc.*, July 1973, p. 422.

82. Faucett, R. E., "The New Economics of Roadway Lighting," *LD&A*, January 1973, p. 29.

83. Faucett, R. E., "The Zonal-Cavity System Applied to Tunnels," *Illum. Eng.*, March 1970, p. 141.

84. Fowle, A. W. and Kaercher, R. L., "Light Distributions for Effective Control of Glare in Roadway Lighting," *Illum. Eng.*, May 1962, p. 336.

85. Fowle, A. W. and Kaercher, R. L., "Roadway Brightness and Illumination as Related to Luminaire Distribution," *Illum. Eng.*, April 1961, p. 279.

86. Franklin, J. S., "Semi-Directional Fixed Lighting for One-Way Highways," *J. Illum. Eng. Soc.*, Oct. 1971, p. 14.

87. Freedman, M., *et al*, "Fixed Illumination for Pedestrian Protection," Reports No. FHWA-RD-76-8/9, Washington, D.C.: Federal Highway Administration, Offices of Research and Development, 1975.

88. Furter, H. W., "Simplification of Street Lighting Installation Designs," *Lichttechnik*, May 1968, p. 57A.

89. Gallagher, V. *et al*, "The Specification of Street Lighting Needs," Report No. FHWA-RD-76-17, Washington, D.C.: Federal Highway Administration, Offices of Research and Development, 1975.

90. Horton, J. G., "Do's and Don'ts of High Mast Lighting," *LD&A*, Dec. 1976, p. 5.

91. Husby, D. E. and Stark, R. E., "A Better Way . . . Lighting for High Speed, Multilane Highways," *Illum. Eng.*, Mar. 1979, p. 156.

92. Jung, F. W. and Blamey, C., "Computer Systems Program for Roadway Lighting," Ontario: Research and Development Division, Ministry of Transportation and Communications, 1976.

93. Jung, F. W., "The Limitation of Disability Glare in Roadway Lighting," Ontario: Systems Research and Development Branch, Ministry of Transportation and Communication, 1977.

94. Ketvirtis, A. and Hobson, R. C., "Safety Features in Highway Lighting System Design," *Illum. Eng.*, Jan. 1971, p. 47.

95. LeVere, R. and Mahler, E., "Uniformity of Illumination (U.I.)," *Illum. Eng.*, Apr. 1970, p. 211.

96. Loudon, J. H., "Street Lighting in Great Britain," *Illum. Eng.*, June 1967, p. 381.

97. Rex, C. H., "Roadway Lighting for the Motorist," *Illum. Eng.*, Feb. 1967, p. 95.

98. Schreuder, D. A., "Trends in European Tunnel Lighting Practice," *Illum. Eng.*, June 1967, p. 390.

99. Singh, H., "Public Lighting Systems," *Public Lighting*, Sept. 1976, p. 75.

100. Smith, R. A. and Goguen, G., "Relating Design, Economic Analysis, and Energy Conservation Techniques in Highway Lighting," *LD&A*, April 1976, p. 18.

101. Stark, R., and Gossyphas, H., "A Second Look at Low Pressure Sodium," *LD&A*, Apr. 1972, p. 13.

102. Stark, R. E., "Test Results of Higher-Mounted Roadway Luminaires," *Illum. Eng.*, Apr. 1968, p. 223.

103. van Bommel, W. J. M., "Costs and Energy Consumption in Road Lighting," *ILR*, 1978/4, p. 114.

104. van Bommel, W. J. M., "Design Considerations for Roadway

Lighting," *J. Illum. Eng. Soc.*, Oct. 1978, p. 40.

105. van Bommel, W. J. M., "Optimization of the Quality of Roadway Lighting Installations—Especially Under Adverse Weather Conditions," *J. Illum. Eng. Soc.*, Jan. 1976, p. 99.

106. van Bommel, W. J. M., "Tunnel Lighting," *ILR*, 1977/4, p. 110.

107. van den Bijllaardt, D., "High Mast Lighting," *ILR*, 1977/4, p. 97.

108. Van Dusen, H. A., Jr., "Roadway Lighting System Design," *J. Illum. Eng. Soc.*, 1974, p. 115.

109. Walthert, R., "Tunnel Lighting Systems," *ILR*, 1977/4, p. 112.

110. Walton, N. E. and Rowan, N. J., "Warrants for Highway Lighting," National Cooprative Highway Research Program Report 152, Washington, D.C.: Transportation Research Board, National Research Council, 1974.

111. Welty, D., "System Analysis of High Mast and Conventional Street Lighting," *J. Illum. Eng. Soc.*, Jan. 1973, p. 121.

112. Wilson, A. R., "The Offset System—Status and Application Concepts," *LD&A*, April 1976, p. 6.

113. Yeager, J. C. and Van Dusen, H. A., Jr., "Factors Affecting the Efficiency of Street Lighting Systems," *Illum. Eng.*, Apr. 1961, p. 262.

114. Ketvirtis, A. and McCullough, V. A., "Highway Lighting Design—Canadian Style," *LD&A*, Apr. 1980, p. 34.

115. IES Design Practice Committee, "Available Lighting Computer programs: A Compendium and a Survey," *LD&A*, Mar. 1981, p. 35.

116. Konz, S., *et al*, "Improving Night Visibility of Trains at Crossings," *LD&A*, June 1981, p. 37.

117. Young, S. H., "Lighting a Special Purpose Urban Freeway," *LD&A*, June 1981, p. 18.

Economics and maintenance

118. Bain, A. W., "Fault Finding in Underground Cables," *Public Lighting*, Sept. 1974, p. 165.

119. Clark, F., "Economical Mercury Street Lighting Maintenance," *Illum. Eng.*, Nov. 1964, p. 741.

120. Cook, L. F., "Computerization of Highway Lighting Maintenance," *Public Lighting*, Mar. 1976, p. 8.

121. DeLaney, W. B. and MacLennan, D. A., "A Financial Decision Technique for Choosing Between Alternative Lighting Systems," *J. Illum. Eng. Soc.*, Jan. 1974, p. 119.

122. Edman, W. H., "Cost Analysis of Roadway Lighting and Vehicular Lighting Practice in Urban Area," *J. Illum. Eng. Soc.*, Jan. 1974, p. 129.

123. Janoff, M. S. and McCunney, W., "Economic Analysis of Roadway Lighting," *J. Illum. Eng. Soc.*, July 1979, p. 244.

124. Ketvirtis, A. and Razauskas, S. G., "Interchange Illumination—Engineering and Economics," *J. Illum. Eng. Soc.*, Oct. 1972, p. 50.

125. Macaulay, N. S., "Maintenance by Need," *Public Lighting*, Dec. 1978, p. 122.

126. MacCracken, J. A., "The Economic Dilemma of Roadway Lighting," *Illum. Eng.*, Mar. 1970, p. 122.

127. Ooerkvitz, C. A., "Field Evaluation of Roadway Lighting Maintenance Factors," *Illum. Eng.*, Feb. 1971, p. 90.

128. Scholz, C. F., "Luminaire Dirt Depreciation and Maintenance," *J. Illum. Eng. Soc.*, Apr. 1975, p. 177.

129. Smiatek, G., "The Road Surface as an Economic Cost Factor in Street Lighting," *Lichttechnik*, June 1968, p. 63A.

130. Van Dusen, H. A., Jr., "Maintenance and Adjustment Factors in Street Lighting Design Calculations," *J. Illum. Eng. Soc.*, Oct. 1971, p. 62.

131. Van Dusen, H. A., Jr., "Street Lighting Luminaire Dirt Depreciation," *Illum. Eng.*, Feb. 1971, p. 122.

132. Whittemore, J., "Street Lighting Maintenance," *Public Lighting*, Sept. 1978, p. 71.

Equipment and energy

133. Austin, B. R., "Lamp Life Performance of High Pressure Sodium Lamps in the City of London," Report No. 4, *Public Lighting*, September 1976, p. 85.

134. Barry, D. M. and Kohbodi, S. M. F., "Degradation Analysis in Switched Low Pressure Sodium Lamps," *Lighting Research and Technology*, Vol. 11, No. 4, 1979, p. 189.

135. Crowther, R., "High Lighting Masts," *Public Lighting*, Dec. 1977, p. 110.

136. de Boer, J. B., "Modern Light Sources for Highways," *J. Illum. Eng. Soc.*, Jan. 1974, p. 142.

137. Brass, J. R., "The Classification Dilemma for Sharp Cutoff Roadway Luminaires," *Illum. Eng.*, Mar. 1970, p. 115.

138. Hilton, M. H., "Alternatives for Energy Conservation in Roadway Lighting," Report VHTRC 80-R8, Charlottesville: Virginia Highway and Transportation Research Council, Aug. 1979.

139. Lewin, I., "A Luminance Approach to Highway Sign Lighting," *J. Illum. Eng. Soc.*, Jan. 1974, p. 122.

140. Lin, F. C. and Knochel, W. J., "High Efficacy Low Wattage HPS Lamps for Street Lighting," *J. Illum. Eng. Soc.*, Apr. 1975, p. 204.

141. Lurkis, A. and Stonehill, E. A., "Shielded-Zone Low-Elevation Outdoor Lighting Utilizing Specular Parabolic Wedge Louvered Luminaires," *Illum. Eng.*, Feb. 1966, p. 107.

142. Mollin, R., "Progress Report on Lighting Highway Signs: The Use of Mercury Lamps," *Illum. Eng.*, Feb. 1967, p. 115.

143. "Sodium Update—Public Response Proves Positive," *ILR*, 1978/4, p. 107.

144. Van Dusen, H. A., Jr., "Optical Plastics Application in Street-Lighting Luminaires," *Illum. Eng.*, Feb. 1966, p. 91.

145. Van Dusen, H. A., Jr., "Street Lighting Luminaire Vibration," *Illum. Eng.*, Feb. 1968, p. 67.

146. Van Dusen, H. A., Jr., and Wandler, D., "Street Lighting Pole Vibration Research," *Illum. Eng.*, Nov. 1965, p. 650.

147. Van Dusen, H. A., Jr., "Structural Ratings of Outdoor Lighting Equipment," *LD&A*, Oct. 1975, p. 24.

148. Van Dusen, H. A., Jr., "Thermal Performance of Street Lighting Luminaires," *Illum. Eng.*, Mar. 1970, p. 172.

149. Van Dusen, H. A., "Vibration Testing of Luminaires," *J. Illum. Eng. Soc.*, Jan. 1980, p. 115.

150. Wilson, A. R. and Johnson, J. F., "The Offset Luminaire System—a New Concept in Roadway Lighting," *LD&A*, Sept. 1974, p. 33.

151. Zeller, R. D., "Complexities and Interrelationships in Lowering Device Design for High Mast Lighting Equipment," *J. Illum. Eng. Soc.*, July 1978, p. 212.

152. Unglert, M. C. and Kane, M. C., "The Interaction of High Pressure Sodium Lamps, Ballasts, and Luminaires," *LD&A*, Nov. 1980, p. 44.

Luminance

153. Berger, M. and Fischer, U., "A Physical Luminance Measuring Device," *Lichttechnik*, Apr. 1968, p. 37A.

154. Cobb, J., "Road Surface Reflection Characteristics," *Public Lighting*, Dec. 1979, p. 222.

155. Finch, D. M., *et al*, "A Bridge-Roadway Lighting Study Based on Roadway Luminance Factors," *Illum. Eng.*, February 1968, p. 77.

156. Fischer, D., "European Approach to the Luminance Aspect of Roadway Lighting," *J. Illum. Eng. Soc.*, Jan. 1975, p. 111.

157. Hentschel, H. J., "Systematic Description of the Reflection of Road Surfaces," *Lichttechnik*, Nov. 1967, p. 138A.

158. Kebscull, W., "Luminance Ratios on Wet Roads," *Lichttechnik*, No. 9, 1966, p. 109A.

159. Keck, M. E. and Odle, H. A., "A Field Evaluation of Pavement Luminance and Glaremark," *J. Illum. Eng. Soc.*, Oct. 1975, p. 37.

160. Ketvirtis, A. and Bastianpillai, J. A., "Road Surface Reflectance," *Transport Canada*, Sept. 1978.

Vision and visibility

161. Ahmed, I. and Bennett, C. A., "Discomfort Glare: Duration-Intensity Relationship," *J. Illum. Eng. Soc.*, Oct. 1978, p. 36.

162. Ashley, A. and Douglas, C. A., "Can Infrared Improve Visibility Through Fog?," *Illum. Eng.*, Apr. 1966, p. 243.

163. Bennett, C. A., "Discomfort Glare: Concentrated Sources—Parametric Study of Angularly Small Sources," IERI Report, *J. Illum. Eng. Soc.*, Oct. 1977, p. 2.

164. Blackwell, H. R. and Blackwell, O. M., "Relationships Between Visual Performance and Visibility Level for Landolt-ring Arrays," *LD&A*, July 1977, p. 36.

165. Blackwell, H. R. "Roadway Illumination and Visibility in Fog," IERI Report, *J. Illum. Eng. Soc.*, Oct. 1971, p. 45.
166. Blackwell, H. R., *et al*, "Visibility and Illumination Variables in Roadway Visual Tasks," *Illum. Eng.*, May 1964, p. 277.
167. Blackwell, O. M., and Blackwell, H. R., "A Proposed Procedure for Predicting Performance Aspects of Roadway Lighting in Terms of Visibility," IERI Report, *J. Illum. Eng. Soc.*, Apr. 1977, p. 148.
168. Blackwell, O. M. and Blackwell, H. R., "Assessment of Target Visibility in a Scale-Model Simulator Under Different Layouts of Conventional Fixed Lighting," Final Report, Project EES-263, Columbus: Ohio Dept. of Trans. and FHWA, Engineering Experiment Station, Ohio State University, Jan. 1973.
169. Bodmann, H. W., "Visibility Assessment in Lighting Engineering," *J. Illum. Eng. Soc.*, July 1973, p. 437.
170. Bonvallet, G. G., *et al*, "Visibility Distance as Affected by Roadway Lighting Parameters," *Illum. Eng.*, May 1965, p. 355.
171. Buck, J. A., *et al*, "Roadway Visibility as a Function of Light Source Color," *J. Illum. Eng. Soc.*, Oct. 1975, p. 20.
172. Connolly, P. L., "Vision, Man, Vehicle, and Highway," Highway Safety Research Institute, University of Michigan, 1967.
173. Forbes, T. W., "Factors in Highway Sign Visibility," *Illum. Eng.*, Aug. 1970, p. 495.
174. Forbes, T. W., *et al*, "Low Contrast and Standard Visual Acuity Under Mesopic and Photopic Illumination," *Journal of Safety Research*, March 1969, p. 5.
175. Fry, G. A., "Blur of the Retinal Image of an Object Illuminated by Low Pressure and High Pressure Sodium Lamps," IERI Report, *J. Illum. Eng. Soc.*, Apr. 1976, p. 158.
176. Fry, G. A. and King, V. N., "The Pupillary Response and Discomfort Glare," *J. Illum. Eng. Soc.*, July 1975, p. 307.
177. Gallagher, V. P., "A Visibility Metric for Safe Lighting of City Streets," *J. Illum. Eng. Soc.*, Jan. 1976, p. 85.
178. Gallagher, V. P., *et al*, "Interaction Between Fixed and Vehicular Illumination Systems on City Streets," *J. Illum. Eng. Soc.*, Oct. 1974, p. 3.
179. Ketvirtis, A., "Visibility Study for Long Vehicular Tunnels," *J. Illum. Eng. Soc.*, Jan. 1975, p. 120.
180. Marsden, A. W., "Brightness—a Review of Current Knowledge," *Lighting Research and Technology*, Vol. 1, No. 3, 1969, p. 171.
181. *Proceedings of the First Annual Symposium on Visibility in the Driving Task*, sponsored by the Highway Research Board, Illuminating Engineering Research Institute and Texas A&M University, College Station, Texas, May 13–15, 1968.
182. *Proceedings of the Second Annual Symposium on Visibility and Driving*, presented by Highway Research Board, Illuminating Engineering Research Institute, and the Institute of Transportation and Traffic Engineering at the University of California, held at Berkeley, California, July 8–10, 1969.
183. Rex. C. H. and Franklin J. S., "Relative Visual Comfort Evaluations of Roadway Lighting," *Illum. Eng.*, Mar. 1960, p. 161.
184. Richards, O. W., "Visual Needs and Possibilities for Night Automobile Driving," United States Government Publication 176566, 1967, p. 13.
185. Rinalducci, E. J. and Beare, A. N., "Losses in Nighttime Visibility Caused by Transient Adaptation," *J. Illum. Eng. Soc.*, July 1974, p. 336.
186. Schober, H.-A. W., "Influence of Disability Glare on Highway Visibility in Fatigues and Normal Observers," *Illum. Eng.*, June 1965, p. 414.
187. Schwab, R. N., "Night Visibility for Opposing Drivers with High and Low Headlight Beams," *Illum. Eng.*, May 1965, p. 364.
188. Thomas, E. L., "Movements of the Eye," *Scientific American*, Aug. 1968, p. 88.
189. Waldram, J. M., "Surface, Seeing and Driving: Some Recent Studies," *Light and Lighting*, Nov. 1960, p. 305.
190. Waldram, J. M., "Visual Problems in Streets and Motorways," *Illum. Eng.*, May 1962, p. 361.

191. Lulla, A. B. and Bennett, C. A., "Discomfort Glare: Range Effects," *J. Illum. Eng. Soc.*, Jan. 1981, p. 74.
192. Kaiser, P. K., *et al*, "Discomfort Glare from Highway Lighting," *J. Illum. Eng. Soc.*, Oct. 1980, p. 17.
193. Ewing, J. L., "Roadway Visibility *vs.* Luminaire Cutoff," *J. Illum. Eng. Soc.*, Oct. 1980, p. 47.
194. Fry, G. A., "A Re-evaluation of the Scattering Theory of Glare," *Illum. Eng.*, Feb. 1954, p. 98.

Miscellaneous references

195. Barbrow, L. E., "The Metric System in Illuminating Engineering," *Illum. Eng.*, Nov. 1967, p. 638.
196. Claxton, M. J., "The Humberside Story, (A Road Lighting Conversion Program)," *ILR*, 1978/4, p. 110.
197. Finch, D. M., "Atmospheric Light Pollution," *Journal of the IES*, January 1978, p. 105.
198. Franklin, J. S., "Statistical Presentation of Roadway Photometric Data," *J. Illum. Eng. Soc.*, Jan. 1974, p. 135.
199. IES Nomenclature Committee, "Proposed American National Standard Nomenclature and Definitions for Illuminating Engineering," *J. Illum. Eng. Soc.*, Oct. 1979, p. 2.
200. Kaufman, J. E., "Introducing SI Units," *Illum. Eng.*, Oct. 1968, p. 537.
201. Millington, F., and Miles, E. E., "Cost Effective Public Lighting," *Public Lighting*, Mar. 1979, p. 23.
202. "New York's Bridges," *Illum. Eng.*, Aug. 1965, p. 467.
203. Odle, H. A., "HID Field Measurements vs. Data Calculated from Photometry," *J. Illum. Eng. Soc.*, Jan. 1975, p. 84.
204. Odle, H. A., "Roadway Lighting Specifications of the Future," *LD&A*, July 1979, p. 18.
205. Schwab, R. N., *et al*, "Monetary Values Drivers Place on Comfort in Night Driving," *J. Illum. Eng. Soc.*, Jan. 1973, p. 104.
206. Spencer, D. E. and Levin, R. E., "Guidance in Fog on Turnpikes," *Illum. Eng.*, Apr. 1966, p. 251.
207. Spencer, D. E. and Peek, S. C., "The Transient Aspect of Automotive Lighting," *Illum. Eng.*, Apr. 1971, p. 292.
208. Spinelli, J. A., "New Street Lighting in Long Beach," *ILR*, 1978/4, p. 103.
209. Sullivan, D. D., "State of the Art in High-Mast Lighting," *LD&A*, Dec. 1976, p. 9.
210. van Bommel, W. J. M., "Mobile Laboratory for Roadway Lighting," *LD&A*, July 1979, p. 31.
211. W. Weibel, "Portable Electric Photometers—a Survey," *LD&A*, Aug. 1975, p. 5.
212. Fisher, A. J., and Hall, R. R., "The Effect on Vision of Terminators and Isolated Lengths of Fixed Lighting," *IES Lighting Review* (Australia), Oct. 1976, p. 125.
213. S. M. Faber, "Sky Glow at Lick Observatory," *LD&A*, Mar. 1980, p. 18.

Important periodicals

214. *Transactions of the Illuminating Engineering Society*, New York: Illuminating Engineering Society of North America, 1906 through 1948.
215. *Illuminating Engineering*, New York: Illuminating Engineering Society of North America, 1949 through 1971.
216. *Journal of the Illuminating Engineering Society*, New York: Illuminating Engineering Society of North America, published since 1971.
217. *Lighting Design & Application*, New York: Illuminating Engineering Society of North America, published since 1971.
218. *Lighting Engineers*, Lennox House, 9 Lawford Road, Rugby, Warwickshire, CV21 2DZ, United Kingdom of Great Britain.
219. *International Lighting Review*, P.O. Box 721, 5600 AS Eindhoven, The Netherlands.
220. *Lichttechnik*, Helios Verlag GMBH, Eichborndamm 141–167, 1 Berlin 52, West Germany.
221. *Lighting Research and Technology*, Lighting Division, The Chartered Institution of Building Services, 222 Balham High Road, London SW129BS, United Kingdom of Great Britain.

INDEX